Race Navigation

RACE NAVIGATION

Stuart Quarrie

STANFORD MARITIME LONDON

Stanford Maritime Limited
Member Company of the George Philip Group
12–14 Long Acre   London WC2E 9LP
Editor Phoebe Mason

First published in Great Britain 1982
Copyright © Stuart Quarrie 1982

Filmset in Monophoto Baskerville 11/13 by
Tameside Filmsetting Limited,
Ashton-under-Lyne, Lancashire
Printed in Great Britain by
Ebenezer Baylis & Son Ltd
The Trinity Press, Worcester, and London

Contents

Introduction

This book is aimed primarily at navigators who are either already involved or who intend to become involved in yacht racing. However, most sections apply equally well to the cruising sailor who merely wants to navigate his boat with a bit less effort while getting to his destination faster.

My main reason for wanting to write on this subject was to provide aspiring racing navigators with some of the techniques, hints and advice which I would have loved to have when I was first asked to navigate a Half Tonner in a race, and which I found it impossible to obtain due to a lack of suitable reading matter.

I feel that I must take this opportunity to thank all those who have made this book possible, especially all the yacht owners who have allowed me to navigate for them, my wife Sue for letting me go racing in most of my spare time, my father for teaching me to sail and navigate as a child, and finally the National Sailing Centre for giving me so much encouragement and time off for racing.

Stuart Quarrie

Chapter 1 The Role of the Navigator

The Responsibilities of a Navigator

There are at least two sides to the job of navigating a racing yacht and in most cases there will be several additional tasks which fall upon the navigator's shoulders. The first and most obvious responsibility that he has to fulfill is to know, or be able to work out, where the yacht is at any given moment. The second, and in my opinion more important, part of race navigating is deciding where to go next in order to reach the next mark as quickly as possible. The 'traditional' cruising type of navigator will all too often fulfill the first of these two basic requirements admirably while neglecting the latter. With modern navigational aids there should very rarely be any problem in either position fixing or working up an accurate estimated position, and this will become more and more the case as racing regulations are gradually brought up to date in allowing such aids as satellite navigators, automatic radio direction finders, off-course computers and the like.

Assuming that the navigator can and does fix the position of his yacht, this leaves decision-making as his major job. However many aids there are at his disposal, deciding where to head next will always remain a real skill, combining as it does some science together with an element of (inspired?) guesswork. The decision will be based on a number of elements, the chief ones being: the known performance of the yacht; the estimated tidal streams and currents; an accurate forecast of any meteorological changes; and an accurate position from which to start calculations. Which of these are based on science and which are mainly guesswork will depend to a large extent on how much effort one is prepared to put into navigating. The weather is the only factor which, at least at present, need have a large percentage of 'guestimation'; the others are on the whole capable of being accurately determined.

Though the two main areas of responsibility of the racing navigator are clear, there are additional tasks which he may be asked to do. The list here merely gives an idea as to the range of these tasks; the exact details will vary from boat to boat:

Timing at the start
Calculating the position on handicap at turning marks
Acting as radio operator
Recording data and analysing it for performance evaluation

Maintaining the navigational equipment, charts, etc
Acting as tactician – and so on *ad infinitum*.

The Position of the Navigator Among the Crew

How the navigator fits into the crew will depend to a large extent on the size of yacht and whether or not it can afford to carry a specialist. Having navigated on racing yachts at both ends of the size range (Quarter Ton up to Class One) I am convinced that the ideal is to have a specialist who is not in the watch system and not needed as a crewman for normal evolutions. This will allow him to always be awake and alert when required for decision making, position fixing or what have you, while still able to get enough rest between bouts of activity. This will only be possible on larger boats, due to the constraints of weight and space, and on modern, relatively light yachts I would put the minimum size suitable for carrying a specialist at about Two Ton. On longer than average races such as the Fastnet, it may well be worth carrying an extra crew member anyway, thus making it feasible and sensible for smaller yachts to have a specialist navigator.

On smaller yachts some sort of compromise has to be reached in task allocation to enable the necessary navigation to be carried out while using the person responsible as a deck crew member at the same time. Various systems work to a greater or lesser extent and some of these are discussed in the following paragraphs.

Navigator as non-watch-keeping crew member If the ideal crew size is an odd number and all the other tasks (such as helming) are duplicated from one watch to the other, then it is possible to have the navigator as a floating crew member. His main function is then the same as if he were a specialist navigator, but whenever the watch on deck needs an extra hand for sail changing, gybing, etc. he will be called up. One advantage of this system is that the person navigating is going to be awake at most alterations of course anyway, as it is probably his decision that has made the alteration necessary in the first place, and he will certainly be up for mark roundings at least. If this system is used it is vital that the navigator has very specific duties to perform in each of the various evolutions as he may well not be as aware of the details of the operation (such as which halyards are being used) as the rest of the crew on deck, since it is quite likely that he will only just have been woken.

Two navigators When for some reason it is not feasible to remove the navigator from the watch-keeping system then it is vital that each watch has someone who can do at least the basic navigation. In my experience it is normally better to have one person in charge of the navigational decisions and for his opposite number in the other watch to just do the basic positional navigation of recording data, fixing position, working up EPs and so on. Otherwise, if both people are making decisions the navigation could become like politics, with a change in strategy at each watch change. In any system where more than one person is going to be involved with the navigation it is vital that all those who may be involved use the same terminology and understand the principles and degree of accuracy that the others are working towards.

In practice, if two navigators are being used then at least one of them is almost bound to lose out on rest compared to the other watch-keepers as the handover at each watch change will tend to involve a fair amount of information, and also because the decision-making times will invariably be when the 'chief' navigator is off watch. In races lasting up to a couple of days this lack of rest is not likely to become important, but on a longer race it is a factor to be considered when getting a crew together.

Pre-planned navigation As a general rule, when yachts get really small the races that they are likely to participate in reduce in length correspondingly. This has the great advantage from the navigational point of view that there is less likelihood of major changes in conditions during the race, and the quantity of tidal and other data that is required for the race period will be reduced to manageable proportions. Both of these factors mean that pre-planning in detail becomes feasible, with courses to steer, depths of water at strategic places, etc. being calculable before the race. To a large extent, therefore, the navigation can be done before the race, with minimal work to be done after the start—just the occasional fix or EP—and if the race is short enough and sufficient pre-planning has been done, the navigator can almost do himself out of a job. Also, of course, on a short race there is less need for rest and so people can be multi-functioned with little loss of efficiency. I would put races of up to about 18 hours in this category.

The Attitude of the Crew to Navigation

Just as the navigator must know where his role lies within the crew, so must the rest of the crew know what is expected of them by the navigator. Far too often the navigator will work away in his own little world without considering the yacht as a whole, and without the others knowing why a particular course should be steered or whether small wind shifts are important or whether it is all right to go for tactical am sailing on a yacht where the crew doesn't know me, it is usually worth having some sort of informal briefing before the race to ensure that data is recorded as I want it and that I am woken at the times that I feel are necessary as well when the crew think it warranted.

In order for the crew to work with the navigator, they must be persuaded that the decisions he is taking are the right ones, so that, if for example an accurate course is asked for, it will actually happen rather than the helmsman following his own feelings, and basically so that honesty will prevail. It is galling to find that a request for a particular course change or whatever has been ignored while one was down below, due either to misunderstanding or a lack of trust.

Good communication between crew and navigator on a two-way basis is absolutely essential to the winning of races, and to the safety of the boat and those aboard her.

Chapter 2 **Tools of the Trade**

To be able to navigate successfully, one must have a large number of individual pieces of equipment and these must all have their proper places in the yacht so as to be usable at sea in any conditions. There are some items that are absolutely essential, some that it would be difficult to do without, and some unashamed luxuries. This chapter deals with all three levels of equipment.

Chartwork Instruments

Although most navigators have favourite plotting instruments that they insist are the best/easiest/cheapest on the market, as these favourites tend just to be the particular instrument that they are most familiar with, it is worth looking dispassionately at some of the advantages and disadvantages of the different types available.

Dividers Starting with a fairly non-controversial instrument, it is obviously pretty well essential to have at least one pair of dividers on board. There are basically two types to choose from, 'singlehanded' (bowed) or straight. The singlehanded type offer the advantage of being easier than the straight ones to use with one hand, for small distances, although once the straight type are open beyond 20° or so, they are just as easy to use and in addition the larger sizes (7 in.) always feel to me to be slightly more robust than the singlehanded type. My personal choice, therefore, is for a pair of 6 in. singlehanded dividers for most purposes, with a set of 7 in. straight ones as a spare and for measuring the occasional very long distance. The choice of material doesn't matter so long as they are corrosion-free.

Parallel rulers In my experience as an instructor, most navigators who start their navigating on ships as opposed to ordinary sized yachts prefer parallel rulers of some kind in preference to more 'modern' instruments. I am sure that a straightedge of 12 in. or so is an essential piece of equipment and I quite often use parallel rulers for this purpose. However, I am also convinced that unless you have a truly magnificent chart table, parallel rulers are not the easiest instrument to use. On the average half-chart size (if you are lucky) table with fiddles all the way around it, you end up having to keep moving the chart around to get the ruler into the corners. In practice I would have a pair of parallel rulers about 10 or 12 in. long, mainly for use as a straightedge but also as a reserve plotting instrument when all else has been lost or broken. Even on a very large yacht with a correspondingly large chart table, I would hesitate to give room in my kit to roller rulers of a traditional type.

Douglas/Portland Protractors These little square protractors were developed for air navigators to use with a chart on their knees, probably with only one free hand. An easy way to use one is shown in Fig. 2.1 : in nearly all cases this is an easier and better way to use a Douglas Protractor than the complicated methods shown on the boxes that they come in, and just as accurate. Another trick to note with it is : if using a protractor to plot a bearing on the chart where one has to plot the reciprocal, rather than risking an arithmetic mistake in subtracting or adding 180°, merely turn the protractor through 180° (i.e. upside down) as in Fig. 2.1b and plot the actual bearing. If limited by cost to a single plotting instrument, this is the one I would choose ; in any event I would always have one on board for plotting on one's knee in the cockpit. When buying a Douglas Protractor, I would advise a 5 in. version and if possible ensure that the figures are engraved in the plastic and not just printed on the surface.

The two disadvantages I have found with Douglas/Portland protractors are that you need a straightedge to work with it for maximum efficiency, and that you need to work in degrees True all the time and cannot plot magnetic bearings directly onto the chart (without drawing magnetic meridans on the chart beforehand).

Hurst or Channel Plotters Two plotters that use the same principle and enable one to set the plotter for the local magnetic variation (which very often covers all the charts needed for a whole race) and then plot any magnetic bearings or courses without having to convert them to True first. In my opinion this avoids the likelihood of arithmetic errors in the middle of the night. I normally leave my Hurst plotter set up for Magnetic, and use a Douglas protractor for the occasions when I need to plot True bearings.

Other plotting instruments Numerous other plotting instruments are available and most have a part to play in making someone's life easier. When choosing which instrument to use make sure that you fully understand it (I used a Douglas Protractor for a whole season in the way the instructions told me before I worked out alternative

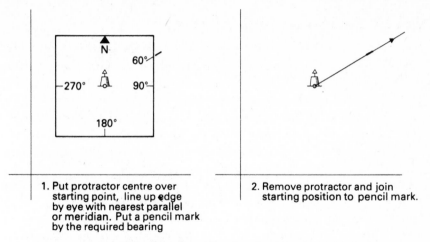

1. Put protractor centre over starting point, line up edge by eye with nearest parallel or meridian. Put a pencil mark by the required bearing

2. Remove protractor and join starting position to pencil mark.

(*a*) To plot a line whose bearing is known

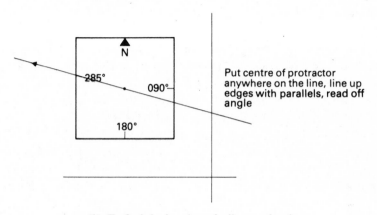

Put centre of protractor anywhere on the line, line up edges with parallels, read off angle

(*b*) To find the bearing of a line on the chart

2.1 Using a Douglas Protractor

methods), and also ensure that it suits both the boat you are sailing on and the type of navigation that you are going to be doing. Remember, it is you who is going to be doing the navigating, not the salesman extolling the virtues of his latest money-maker!

Obviously one also needs pencils, which should be a fairly soft grade in order both to draw blacker lines and make erasing easier. I would suggest either B or 2B as being the most suitable. A propelling or clutch pencil with this soft grade of lead in it can save some effort in pencil sharpening.

The final drawing instrument required is a pair of compasses, used for drawing distances off, ranges of lights, etc.

Books and Other Publications

The number of books that one needs or are available will depend to a large extent on the particular area, but some are virtually essential anywhere.

Tide Tables Anywhere there is any tidal range at all, tide tables for that area are an obvious necessity. The particular 'make' of tables that one uses is not very important so long as they are accurate enough for the area concerned and also quick and easy to use.

Apart from some local areas, where locally produced information can be the best available, I have always found the *Admiralty Tide Tables* (ATT) to fulfill these requirements better than any others. The tidal curves for each Standard Port enable one to work very accurately and quickly, particularly with a calculator to do the multiplying of 'factor' by the range, for example. For most places the Secondary Port time and height differences are fairly straightforward, and anyway these can be worked out in the pre-planning before the race. About the only area in the British Isles for which these time and height differences become excessively complicated is in the Solent and for this area there is an excellent table of hourly heights published in some nautical almanacs under the title 'Swanage to Nab Tower'.

If one uses a fully programmable calculator then the ATT also offers a method of plotting individual tidal curves (with actual heights) for any port, on any day, by using the harmonic constants for a port and combining them with the various factors that determine the tide for that day.

My own feeling about using an almanac such as *Reed's* for tidal height calculations is that as they compromise on space so much by only giving high water for a majority of ports that one is forced to use various average values (e.g. duration of mean rise) which both add to the complication and to the inaccuracy of any calculations. Having said all the above, it must be noted that there are other good, up-to-date almanacs on the market (e.g. *Channel West and Solent*) which, for their particular areas, include all the information one would get from the ATT without the expense of buying a further specialised publication.

Surface Drift (Current) Charts In areas where there is not much in the way of tidal movement, for example the Baltic or the Med, surface drift (current) becomes more important as circulations can be set up which are not dominated by the change of tide every six hours. In such areas the surface drift associated with a particular weather pattern, wind direction and so on, could theoretically, given enough time, be worked out and charts produced to show the rate and direction of the drift. So far as I am aware, the only place for which this has been done at present is some parts of the Baltic, although a considerable amount of general information on the subject can be found in Admiralty *Sailing Directions*, commonly known as 'Pilots'.

Tidal Stream Atlases or Tables In tidal waters they are an essential part of one's equipment; their use is covered in Chapter 3.

Almanacs A nautical almanac of some kind is obviously essential to any serious navigation and the list below shows the information that I consider should be included.

Vertical sextant angle tables
Celestial navigation data, at the very least for the Sun. Ideally this should give azimuth and declination for *each* hour as this is the form in which most simple calculator programs require the data
Sunrise, sunset, twilight, moonrise and moonset times, for taking sights and for knowing when the racing rules are replaced by the International Regulations for the Prevention of Collisions at Sea (COLREGS)
Distance off by lights 'rising' or 'dipping' (tables)
Single letter signals
Radio direction finding beacon frequencies, call signs, etc
Radio weather forecast times and frequencies

Most almanacs have vastly more information than this, with everything from tide tables, light lists and pilotage information to how to tie knots or deliver a baby. In my experience, though, unless money is very short, most of the information is far better covered in publications specifically designed for the purpose. As already stated, the Admiralty Tide Tables cover tidal heights better than most almanacs; and pilot books tend to give pilotage information in far more detail than an almanac could hope to.

Looking at the list of absolutely necessary information, it can be seen that there are a few tables that remain constant from one year to the next, and the only information that is best covered in an almanac is the celestial and radio data. I would therefore suggest extracting the necessary tables from an out-of-date almanac and buying a celestial almanac each year, for example the Nautical Almanac, and an up-to-date Radio List.

List of Lights Though all the major lights and beacons should be marked on the charts for an area, the Admiralty *List of Lights* (or analogous official publications elsewhere) gives far more detail than can be shown on a chart; this is particularly true with regard to the physical appearance and structure of lighthouses, etc. which can be really useful in identifying such structures by day. The Light List also gives full details of arcs of visibility, sectors, duration of flashes, and ranges. In my own racing navigation, I tend to use the Light List during the pre-race planning stage, extracting the data relevant to any lights or structures with which I am unfamiliar or which are incompletely described on the chart, for use during the race (see Chapter 4).

Radio information The necessary information can be split into three main categories: RDF beacons, weather forecasts and reports, and Coast Radio Stations for possible (and allowable) business phone calls, supplementary weather warnings or other announcements. For North Europe at least, all this information was presented in quite a usable format on Rofac (radio facility) Charts (not published in 1982). It is also published in the relevant volumes of the Admiralty *List of Radio Signals* (*ALRS*), the new *List of Radio Signals for Small Craft* (NP 280), or less comprehensively in nautical almanacs.

Pilot books It is said by many racing navigators that you don't need pilotage information during a race since you are not intending to visit lots of harbours. However, some pilot books (both commercially published and official) have good detailed information, both in text and in pictures, on what the coastline looks like, surface drift and local winds or weather, and it is mainly for this that I would always carry pilot books of the area of a race, particularly if it is an area new to me. This means that the type of pilot book that only contains information about actual harbour entries is not suitable for racing, though it might be useful in selecting and entering a port of refuge. Once again, I rely fairly heavily on the Admiralty publications.

Logbook

A logbook used during a race has several functions: it must contain the basic navigation data of course steered, distance run, etc.; it must contain as much observed data about the boat's performance as possible, for future tuning; and it must have the information necessary to substantiate any claims for 'marks unseen', help given to vessels in distress, accidents to crew or to the yacht, and the like. It is fairly obvious that scrappy bits of paper with various squiggles, sums and hieroglyphics written on them will not be enough, and some sort of. ordered logbook is essential, although a *navigator's* notebook, perhaps on the lines of a typist's notebook, can be extremely useful to have around for writing bearings, etc into.

The layout of a logbook will depend to a large extent on personal preference, as will the actual headings for each column, and I put forward the following as a suggestion only, to be modified as required.

Basic navigational headings

TIME should always be 'clock' time so that there is no confusion among the crew when they look at their watches to note down course changes, etc.

COURSE REQUIRED means the course that, as navigator, you would like the helmsman to try to steer. It will not always be steered, due either to tactical considerations or to helmsman error. This column must be the *Compass* course wanted and not the course in True or Magnetic. Once again, this is to avoid possible mistakes by the crew not applying deviation or variation the right way.

COURSE STEERED: it follows from the above that if the course required is not always steered, then there must be a column for the helmsman to record the course he thinks he has actually steered; this again should be in degrees 'Compass'.

LEEWAY should have a separate column even if it is estimated to be insignificant on a particular leg of the course. This is to make everybody think 'Is leeway important at the moment?' whenever a log entry is made. If it is worth recording a leeway angle, then a good way of doing so is to record it as a plus (+) when on port tack and a minus (−) number when on starboard. This reduces the amount of thought needed when it comes to plotting the leeway, as it is then applied according to its sign.

TIME	LOG DIST.	COURSE °COMPASS		LEEWAY + PORT − STBD	WEATHER	REMARKS
		REQD. °C	STEERED °C			

2.2 Basic logbook headings

LOG (DISTANCE RUN) should obviously be recorded every time there is a course change. It can also be important to record the distance on a regular basis, both for tuning analysis later and so that the length of time spent on a particular tidal stream can be estimated for working up the estimated position (EP) of the yacht. When awake, I always try to record the log distance and course steered every half hour unless there has been a course change within this period. As a minimum the two items of distance and course need to be recorded every hour to correspond with the changes in the tidal stream and to ensure that no course changes are forgotten about for very long. Frequent recording also makes human errors or equipment malfunction easier to spot and compensate for. It is dangerous to use the trip meter part of a log for recording distance run as the thing may be tripped accidentally.

WEATHER should at least include the approximate *wind direction* to enable one to work out which tack the yacht was on at any given time. If the weather pattern is such that the *barometric pressure* may change and is of significance, then it can be recorded in this column – hourly, along with the log and course steered so that trends in pressure change can be monitored. In anticyclonic conditions the pressure may well remain virtually constant for the whole period of the race and in that case there is obviously no point at all in recording the same reading hour after hour.

Details of *visibility* and *actual weather* (rain, sun, etc) are probably best recorded in the *General Remarks* column.

DEVIATION: on some yachts it can be worth having a table devoted to recording the compass deviation on each heading, but on most yachts deviation should be almost eliminated by correct compass adjustment and this column is rarely found to be necessary.

REMARKS: the columns detailed above are all specific and it is also essential to have a column where more general information can be recorded (such as average speed, 'rounded first mark', 'hoisted tri-radial', 'gusting' etc. The layout that I use for all these columns is shown in Fig. 2.2.

Headings required for tuning The amount of information that is recorded during a race for use as tuning data at a later stage will depend on two things: first, how much time and effort will be put into analysing the data later; and second, how much time is reasonably available for collecting data not essential to the winning of that particular race.

The minimum that should be recorded is any sail combination that was obviously very fast or that was definitely not fast, with sheet leads, angles and strength of apparent wind, etc for the good combinations. In races that are being used as tune-up races towards an important event, it is probably worth making much more effort than this, and the headings shown in Fig. 2.3 can be utilised. If only the basic data is being recorded it is normally sufficient to use the Remarks column. (The use of all this data is dealt with in Chapter 5 where various methods of analysis are discussed.)

APPARENT WIND		HEEL ANGLE	WATER SPEED	BACKSTAY TENSION	VANG TENSION	WAVES		SAILS AND SHEET LEADS
DIR.	KTS					DIR.	HT.	

2.3 Logbook headings for accumulating tuning data

Charts

Other than the Race Instructions, charts are the most important 'single' publication on board. It is vital that the best charts available are carried and that they are utilised in the best possible manner. ORC Category 2 races require only that 'charts' are carried but the RORC, for example, draws attention to the importance of adequate charts for likely harbours of refuge.

The most detailed charts for any particular coast are likely to be produced by the national hydrographic authority of that country, though this is not necessarily so. It is important, though, that the charts being used are easy to understand, and therefore it is probably better to have a slightly less detailed chart where the nanes, abbreviations and warnings are in your own language than to have a slightly more detail in an unintelligible foreign language. For Northern Europe the Admiralty chart coverage is the most impressive, and in nearly all cases these are the charts that I prefer to use.

As well as the actual detail covered by a chart, the scale is very important: too large a scale and the whole picture cannot be seen at one time, too small a scale and adequate detail cannot be shown either in the printing on the chart or in actually plotting the yacht's position. This means that different scales of chart are needed for each section of the race and to break this down into basic requirements the following would be a good guide.

Small scale chart showing the *whole race area*. This chart would be mainly a general-purpose chart, only really being used for overall strategic planning and sometimes for plotting radio fixes. The actual scale will depend on the course, but on a 200 mile race this chart might be in the order of 1 : 300,000.

Slightly larger scale charts covering the *whole of each leg* of the race and used for plotting EPs, working out the strategy for each leg in some detail, plotting most fixes and so on. In a lot of cases with legs around 60 miles, it will be impossible to get one chart covering the whole of each leg and so perhaps two or even three might be needed for a particular leg. In order to be able to plot EPs and fixes with reasonable accuracy, they shouldn't be much smaller in scale than 1 : 100,000 (approximately $\frac{3}{4}$ in. to the nautical mile).

Finally, large scale charts of *each area of coast* that the race approaches, or that your course might possibly approach. The scale will depend on what charts exist, the money available and on the type of coastline that is being considered. In dangerous, rocky or shoaling areas a scale of 1 : 20,000 or even greater may be required, whereas on a gently shelving, or steep-to uniform coast 1 : 50,000 may suffice. When choosing the scale of the detailed charts it is very important to check whether there are even larger scale charts, because in that case a lot of detail may have been omitted from the charts that have been chosen. This is particularly true of harbours, where there may be no detail shown at all inside the harbour boundaries except on the largest scale harbour chart. Light and fog signal characteristics are given less fully on small scale charts.

Although I have stated a preference for Admiralty charts, it is well worthwhile making oneself familiar with charts produced by other publishers, particularly for the medium scale charts used for planning each leg, as another publisher just might have a chart of exactly the right scale and area and with adequate detail for the purpose required.

Whatever charts one decides to use, it is vital that they are kept up to date and show the buoys, lights and hazards that actually exist at the time of the race and not those that were there a fortnight ago. Comprehensive corrections are published by the Admiralty in their weekly *Notices to Mariners* which can be obtained on a subscription basis at very little cost from any major chart agent. Alternatively, the Admiralty is currently publishing a 'Home Waters' Notice to Mariners every three months especially for small craft, and this can be used in conjunction with extracts from the weekly Notices, extracts of which are published in some of the yachting magazines. It is obviously easiest to use the Admiralty Notices on Admiralty charts as the numbers of the charts affected are listed on the Notice; however, there is no difference in the changes needed to be marked on the charts regardless of who has published them. Foreign hydrographic authorities also publish similar Notices to Mariners.

'Essential' Navigation Equipment

The hardware required for successful racing navigation breaks down into two types, once all the books and chartwork instruments have been decided on. First, there are the things that are not screwed onto the yacht, some of which a navigator might be expected to provide for himself, and second there is all the gear that is attached such as electronics, compasses and so on.

Hand-held Equipment

On most boats the majority of this will be provided, but if one is going to navigate a 'strange' boat it is worthwhile checking just what gear is available, particularly if she doesn't normally take part in the type of race that is being considered. I stepped aboard one yacht an hour before a 120-mile race to find that there were *no* charts on board, the owner having expected me to bring my own!

Binoculars Ideally these should have a magnification of not more than about 8 × (otherwise it becomes impossible to hold them steady) and the object lens should be as large as possible for good light-gathering in the dark. Most people find that 7 × 50 is about the best combination, although some find these glasses too heavy and prefer something like 8 × 40s. The other 'must' with binoculars for use at sea is that the lenses and all other pieces of glass are fully coated to prevent internal reflections.

Hand bearing compass One of the items that in my experience is often of inadequate performance on yachts that seldom race offshore. The most common failing of hand bearing compasses on yachts that are only being used for day racing is that they might well not have illumination.

There are two basic designs of hand bearing compasses: the kind with a handle that you hold at arm's length and that where the optics allow you to hold the compass close to your eye. On a totally stable platform it is probably possible to achieve slightly more accurate results with the former, but in a seaway on a relatively small yacht I have no doubt that the smaller, lighter type such as the Mini-compass is easier and more accurate to use. They also have the advantage of being compact enough to be stowed around one's neck ready for use at any time, even from the weather deck. I have found that a liquid damped compass is easier for me to use, but some people prefer the very quick settling-down of an air-damped compass, and put up with the slightly jerkier movements.

Whichever type of compass you choose, do make sure that there is a spare on board for when the principal one is dropped or lost.

Sextant Whether or not you intend to do any celestial (astro) nav during a race, a sextant is an important piece of equipment that should always be available. In the majority of 'offshore' races with legs of not much more than 60–100 miles and radio beacons available, astro-navigation is not essential anyway, but to be able to tell your distance off headlands, lighthouses, etc is essential and using a sextant to get a vertical angle is very often the easiest way of doing this.

If all that a sextant is going to be used for is vertical angles, then a plastic sextant is the best tool for the job. It will not give the accuracy that a 'real' sextant is capable of, but it will still be used even with spray driving and the boat lurching about, whereas the navigator may feel inclined to leave his expensive metal sextant locked safely away in its box. At present a plastic sextant such as the Ebbco or Davis can be bought for about half the cost of a hand bearing compass and so there is no reason not to have one. Metal or high quality plastic sextants which don't need frequent adjustments for accurate astro-nav start in price at five or six times that of cheap plastic ones, and are really a luxury unless they are going to be used for serious astro-nav, and your sight taking and timing are very accurate. There are books written solely about sextants which describe what to look for in detail, but a few points here might be helpful. A compact sextant, light in weight, is the first requirement, as steadying a full-sized, heavy, traditional sextant on a heaving deck can be next to impossible. The mirrors should be as large as possible as this gives a better field of view, and they need to be protected or sealed against salt water. For most purposes a telescope of modest magnification (say $2\frac{1}{2} \times$) is best; a larger magnification is only required when a large number of star sights are going to be taken. In that case having two telescopes, for general use and for stars, can be an advantage but is not essential. The other obvious requirement is that the sextant must be robust enough to stand up to the almost inevitable mistreatment that it will suffer. (The basic use of a sextant is covered in Chapter 3 and the working of sights with the aid of a calculator is covered in Chapter 6.)

Stopwatch Some form of stopwatch is obviously needed for the start of the race, and also for timing light sequences at night for positive identification. This means that it is a great help if the watch can be read easily in the dark and for this reason a digital stopwatch with illumination can be the best answer, although I find an analogue watch (one with hands) easier at the start of a race.

Alarm clock Very useful for ensuring that weather forecasts are not missed, as it is fairly unreasonable to expect the on-watch to remember all the forecasts while they are concentrating on sail trimming or steering.

Cassette recorder On a racing yacht there are two prime functions of a tape recorder. The first and most obvious is for recording weather forecasts after your alarm clock has woken you up; the second reason for having one is to enable tuning data to be recorded at times when making written entries may be inconvenient or difficult, such as when sitting on the weather rail. A pocket tape recorder is therefore best, and one that can be used while inside a plastic bag lasts a lot longer.

Calculator This subject is covered in detail in Chapter 6 and all I will say here is that there should be one on board.

There are various other gadgets and pieces of equipment that one can buy, such as rangefinders and so on, but I believe that the above constitutes a reasonable list of essentials.

Boat Equipment

The amount of equipment of the type used for navigation that a boat carries will vary wildly with the size of boat and wealth of the owner. The list below looks at the more common equipment while some of the more esoteric aids are considered in Chapter 7.

Steering compass(es) On large yachts there will normally be three compasses for steering by: a main central compass used chiefly for steering downwind and two wing compasses on the side-decks for tactics and steering upwind. On smaller yachts this may well be reduced to two bulkhead compasses or even sometimes (particularly on older, narrow boats) to one central compass. So long as all the compasses can be read effectively at night as well as by day, and are damped sufficiently for the yacht they are on, then the actual make used is a case of deciding which of those available at the time performs best and is easily read.

It is absolutely essential that all the compasses used for steering are corrected for deviation as accurately as possible. When there are two or more compasses on the same yacht it will be virtually impossible to remove all the error from all of them, particularly those sited off the centreline, but in most yachts they should all be correctable to within $1°-2°$ on all headings: if not, then a Deviation Table will have to be worked out and used.

Log and speedometer It is only the distance run part of a log/speedometer that is absolutely essential for accurate position finding, but the speed part of the meter is equally essential for tuning and getting the best out of the rig. Once again, there are many types available ranging from the towed Walker logs to electromagnetic logs with digital or dial readouts. For the most accuracy over the widest range of conditions, some form of towed log scores heavily as they are not affected by the boundary layer that builds up around a hull. Unfortunately, though, while ideal for cruising yachts, the modern equivalent of the Walker logs, i.e. the Stowe log or equivalent, has several undesirable features for a racing yacht. They have slightly higher drag losses than many other types of impeller, and in a short-tacking duel one would tend to lose rather a lot of impellers on the bows of other yachts.

As to whether one should have 'paddlewheel' impellers or not, and other technical details, since the manufacturers don't seem able to agree on what is best I am certainly not going to enter the argument. It is fairly easy to list the parameters for a good log/speedometer though: this then leaves it up to individuals to decide which make/model suits their needs best.

It must be accurate at both high and low speeds as well as intermediate ones.
It must be affected as little as possible by weed or other debris.
It should be able to be run off its own power supply, or if this is not possible it must be fairly tolerant of its input voltage so as to be able to function with nearly flat batteries.
The instrument must be capable of calibration by unskilled users, on board.
It must be reliable.
In the event of repairs being needed, these must be capable of being carried out by technicians in the area where the yacht normally sails.
The speed readout must be such that it can be used to tell the helmsman when he is sailing at the boat's best, which means accurately showing changes in speed down to at least 0.2 knots.
The impeller must be affected as little as possible by turbulence caused by waves. Towed logs tend to suffer most in a following or quartering sea.
Accuracy must not be badly affected by change in the angle of heel. Hull-fitted logs need careful positioning with this in mind.

The above list is undoubtably not comprehensive but at least it gives a starting point when choosing a new log.

Echo-sounder Here again, the actual make of the instrument is probably irrelevant and it is the type of display and the reliability that are most important, along with sensible positioning so that it can be read by both the helmsman and the tactician.

There are three basic types of display, if one discounts graphical models. In systems that are bought as a whole, with wind instruments, log and echo-sounder as part of the same unit, the most common display format is a meter with a pointer indicating the depth. This obviously ties in neatly with other instruments and can make the yacht look 'tidier' but it does have drawbacks. The chief disadvantage of a simple pointer is that it cannot give any indication of the type of bottom that it is displaying, as it can only point in one place at a time, and also it is very easy to be misled as to which scale the set is turned to. However, it does have the advantage that repeaters can normally be taken from the master unit.

The second common type of display is that used by slightly more basic machines, e.g. of the Seafarer type. These have a rotating dial which lights up a light-emitting diode (LED) or neon tube at the depth indicated. Their chief advantage is that depth irregularities and differences in bottom hardness are easily seen by the width and stability of the marker. The scale being used can usually be easily identified from the speed of rotation of the dial. Their main disadvantage is that it can be quite difficult to see the display in very bright sunlight, and also they tend to be noisy and fairly heavy on batteries.

One fairly recent innovation that makes some navigation easier is alarms for shallows and deeper water. Set up sensibly, these allow the navigator to concentrate on things other than depth until it becomes important.

Radio direction finders As these are covered in detail in Chapter 7 all that needs to be said here is that it is essential, especially for medium distance offshore racing, to have some sort of radio direction finding capability.

Wind instruments The only wind instruments that are essential are telltales on the genoa luff and a Windex or similar masthead wind angle indicator. However, having instruments to tell one the wind speed and direction in numerical form enables all the calculations dealt with in Chapter 8 to be carried out.

The make of system used is a matter of personal choice, but from the navigator's point of view the following consideration is worth taking note of: the helmsman only requires an analogue (dial) representation of the wind direction, with different damping for up- and downwind; the navigator, on the other hand, is dealing in actual figures when doing apparent wind calculations and therefore it is ideal for any repeater instruments down below to have digital readout meters rather than anologue ones.

Navigatorium

Although the word 'navigatorium' is not in the *Oxford English Dictionary*, I have always felt that it describes perfectly the whole area within a yacht that is used for navigation. This section looks at the needs of such a navigation area and at some solutions to the various problems encountered in the design or layout of a typical yacht.

By the very nature of most navigation, the chart table is the central part of most navigatoria. Unfortunately, on a lot of yachts its design appears not to have had much thought. The following details some of the more important points to look for.

Ideally a chart table would be large enough for any chart in the yacht's folio to be laid out flat, with spare space around it for books, etc. Unfortunately this size of table is totally impracticable on a yacht of normal proportions, so a compromise has to be reached. All officially published (e.g. Admiralty) charts can be folded into a standard half chart size and the best compromise in the chart table size is based on this. This standard size is approximately 27 × 20 in. and it should be considered as the very smallest workable area for a chart table. Even with a table of these dimensions, though, the charts would need to be turned at right angles to the sitting position about half of the time and so it is preferable to have a large enough table to put the charts either way round, which requires a working area of about 27 in. square as a minimum.

On a really large yacht where weight is not a problem several drawers next to the chart table, one for each folio of twenty or thirty charts, provides the ideal chart stowage. They can be stored flat and are easy to get at and to put away in the right order. This solution is not viable on most racing yachts as the space and weight of drawers over-rides the benefits gained.

The commonest and in most ways very satisfactory way of stowing charts is to have a hinged top to the chart table with a storage 'box' as an integral part of the table. While in principle this is fine, there are some drawbacks that have to be overcome in the detailed design of the table. To start with, it must be possible for the lid of the table to be fixed in the open position in order to leave both hands free for sorting through the charts. Second, the charts should not have to be slid in or out of their stowage and this means that the opening part of the lid must be as near to half chart size as possible. Obviously there must be enough depth to hold all the charts likely to be carried, and for most yachts this will mean at least a 3-in. deep box. Finally, there needs to be a light that shines into the chart stowage when it is open.

Fiddles have to be high enough to stop charts, pencils, books and instruments from falling off the chart table, but they must also be low enough to enable the table to be worked at. I have found that a fiddle about $\frac{3}{4}$ in. high along the front of the table is sufficient, with tapered fiddles along the sides, about $\frac{3}{4}$ in. at the front increasing to 2 in. by the back.

If the lid of the table hinges up, the fiddles must be attached to the hinged section or else things will slip off every time the lid is raised. This can cause problems at the position of the hinge and one solution is shown in Fig. 2.4. It is worth going to this amount of trouble as any gaps in the fiddles on the sides will inevitably lead to items falling off. There does need to be at least one small gap, though, to allow for cleaning the surface of the chart table and this is best at the front (assuming the table is fore-and-aft) as there tends to be far less movement in this direction.

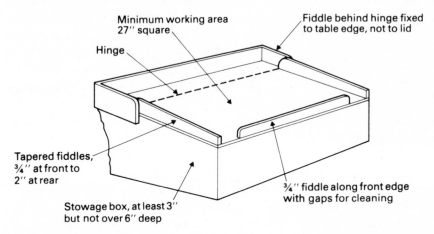

2.4 Suggested chart table design

Positioning the navigatorium The exact position of the chart table, etc will depend very much on the size of boat and the overall layout below, but as with so many things there are certain aspects that are common to most boats. It must be easy for the navigator to get from the cockpit to the navigatorium and back again. Conversations with the helmsman or tactician should ideally be possible between the navigation area and the cockpit without getting up.

The chart table and bookshelves must be protected from the worst of the elements, either by being a long way away from hatches or by the judicious use of a clear plastic screen between the hatch and the chart table. Ideally the navigatorium would be positioned somewhere near the centre of the boat to reduce the amount of movement and so minimise the chance of seasickness while working there.

Stowage of books and equipment There should be a ready-to-hand bookshelf for all the most commonly used books (almanacs, tidal atlases, pilot book, logbook etc) and this needs to be open with no restriction on access. The type of shelf with a removable bar across the front to allow access is a sure way towards books ending up on the cabin sole. One arrangement that works well is to have solid 'pockets' or bins either behind the chart table or on a bulkhead near it, into which books can be put with just their top halves showing. Two pockets of different sizes should be sufficient in most cases: at least 4 in. wide from front to back, and 7–8 in. long and 5 in. deep vertically for small books such as *Reed's Almanac*, or 10 in. long and 7 in. deep for bigger books such as pilots or navigation tables.

Unless books that are not being used for a particular race are always taken ashore, there also needs to be another place for those not in use at the time. This could just be a locker somewhere on board or perhaps an enclosed bookshelf near the navigatorium. If weight is at a premium then it is better to take the unwanted publications ashore before each race and this can mean the charts that aren't needed as well as books. One advantage of having the charts ashore is that it facilitates their correction.

Chartwork instruments can be stowed in the chart table in a partitioned-off section at the front, with the ready-use instruments in a rack at the back of the table. Some clips for the plotter mean that it is less likely to end up in the bilge.

One item that is very often not thought of in the design of locker space is the sextant. Assuming that one has a good sextant on board, its case should ideally be stowed so that the instrument can be taken out and used while the case is still secure in its locker. An open box, padded with foam around the sextant case and with clips to hold the case in place, is a fairly good solution.

Other individual items of equipment such as binoculars all need their own stowage places where they are easy to get at but safe.

Other aspects Most of the equipment needed at the navigatorium has already been discussed but the following list emphasizes just how much bulkhead space is required: control box for wind and boat speed instruments; repeater dials for wind speed and direction, boat speed, distance run and depth; hull thermometer; barometer; RDF, MF receiver, VHF radiotelephone; Loran C if sailing in the Med or the USA, and possibly SSB radio if contemplating long-distance races.

An often neglected but extremely useful piece of equipment, a telltale compass at the chart table enables the navigator to pick up wind shifts, helmsman error and so on while down below plotting. This is obviously a good thing to be able to do but it only works if the telltale compass is properly installed and corrected. On one yacht that I navigated, the telltale compass wasn't even screwed down so that it could (and did) rotate as it pleased thus giving a different reading every few moments. If using a main steering compass that allows for repeaters, to have the telltale and wing compasses all as repeaters can save a lot of problems.

On a long race, particularly on larger yachts, the navigator will spend quite a lot of time at the chart table and it is worthwhile having a well padded seat. More important than this, though, he must be able to brace himself onto the seat regardless of the angle of heel and so a foot bar or strut on either side is a good idea.

Ideally the navigator should be able to reach the chart table from his bunk without getting out of his sleeping bag – not often easily done! However, it is important that it is not difficult for him to get from his bunk to the chart table. It is also worth having the seat actually at the chart table set up so that cat-napping is possible.

Chapter 3 **Basic Techniques**

Although this book is in no way purporting to be a general navigation textbook, there are basic techniques which are common to all navigation and this chapter deals with some of the more important ones.

Use of Vectors

This is a subject that conjures up a complicated mathematical picture in most people's minds. In fact, though, vectors are used in everyday life by almost everyone without conscious thought, and are certainly used by anyone who has done any navigation at all.

A vector by definition is merely a force (tidal stream, wind, etc) which has both strength and direction. In this book vectors will normally be shown (according to convention) as a line, with the length of the line representing the strength of the force and the orientation of the line showing the direction. So the vector for a southwesterly wind of 10 knots would be drawn as in Fig. 3.1.

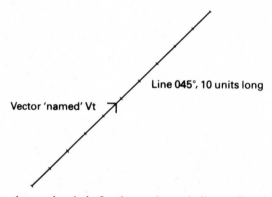

3.1 Vector of southwesterly wind of 10 knots. Arrow indicates direction of force.

Vectors can be combined to give a 'resultant' so long as the units involved are all the same (e.g. knots, hours, etc). To give an example that everyone will recognise let us look at Fig. 3.2. This combines one vector of boat speed and direction with another vector of tidal stream rate and direction. The resultant is of course the track of the boat over the ground, for the same time period as the two component vectors (1 hour).

34

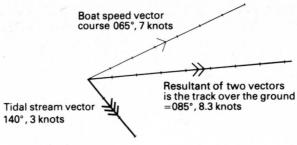

Boat speed vector
course 065°, 7 knots

Resultant of two vectors
is the track over the ground
=085°, 8.3 knots

Tidal stream vector
140°, 3 knots

3.2 Two vectors and their resultant

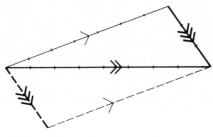

3.3 Construction of a vector triangle using a parellogram of forces. The arrows are all going the same way, and the second vector starts at the end of the first one.

In order to draw this vector diagram we use the fact that we can 'add' the vectors together diagrammatically, using the concept of a parallelogram of forces (Fig. 3.3). As can be seen from this diagram, the same result is obtained whichever vector is drawn first so long as all vectors are drawn in the right direction. To carry this concept one stage further, any number of vectors may be added together in this way with the line joining the beginning of the first vector to the end of the last one being the resultant, as in Fig. 3.4.

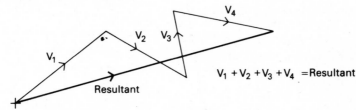

$V_1 + V_2 + V_3 + V_4$ =Resultant

Resultant

3.4 Combining any number of vectors gives a single resultant

Polar and rectangular coordinates So far, we have considered vectors as having a direction and a length. The direction can relate to north (as in most navigation), or to wind direction, or to the yacht's head (as in most true – apparent wind calculations) while the length could be measured in nautical miles (navigation), speed in knots (wind calculations), or kilogram/metres (righting moment calculations). In all cases this format of representing vectors is called 'polar' since the

35

direction is given as an angle relative to north (or the equivalent); Figs 5.3–5.5 are examples. It would be easy to convert a vector from this form to one using x and y coordinates in a graph. This is shown in Fig. 3.5 and is the basis of both calculator navigation and of traverse tables.

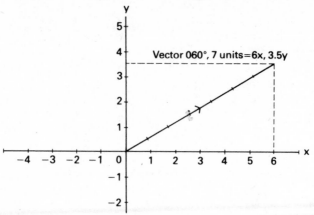

3.5 Converting polar to rectangular coordinates

Adding vectors together using rectangular coordinates is very easy, after having converted from polar coordinates, as it is just a matter of adding up all the xs and all the ys to give the resultant coordinates, and obviously any number of vectors can be added at once in this way. Fig. 3.6 shows the addition of two vectors.

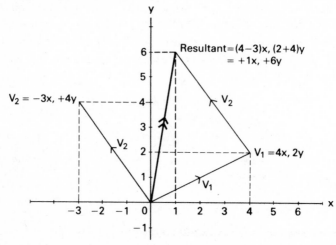

3.6 Adding vectors when using rectangular coordinates

It will not normally be worthwhile converting navigational vectors from polar to rectangular coordinates unless a calculator is being used (when the machine does the conversion for you), although in fact it is not too difficult to do the conversion as latitude and longitude can be used as the x and y values.

DR and EP—Dead Reckoning and Estimated Position

Keeping a DR plot going and working up EPs is the basis of position finding navigation between fixes. The principle used is well known and simple, and is of course just one of the uses of vector diagrams (Fig. 3.7). A few practical tips will make the procedure easier and more accurate and the following paragraphs will look at some of these.

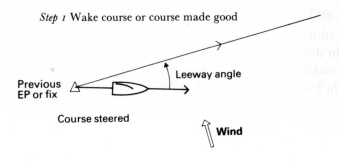

Step 1 Wake course or course made good

Leeway angle

Previous EP or fix

Course steered

Wind

Step 2 Mark off distance run in period since last EP or fix: this is the dead reckoning (DR) position.

Wake course

EP

Step 3 Lay off tidal stream and/or current from DR position to obtain EP.

DR

EP

New EP

3.7 Working up an estimated position (EP)

Leeway allowance The estimate of leeway should always appear in the log if thought to be significant, and I have found it easiest to use if it is entered in the log with a plus or a minus sign. Always plus when on port tack as leeway will be added to the course steered in order to give the wake course on port, and conversely always minus when on starboard tack. Doing it this way means that no thought is required when plotting: merely take the course steered from the logbook and add or subtract the leeway according to its sign before plotting the resultant wake course line on the chart.

Sequence with multiple courses and/or tidal streams The accepted order of plotting lines is to apply any leeway and plot the wake course first, and then the current or tidal stream vector from the end of this line. If more than one course has been steered since the last fix or EP then *all* the wake courses should be plotted first before any tidal streams. One can then plot the total tidal stream for the period concerned, and this will generally result in less division of the tidal stream vectors into inconvenient and short time periods with a probable increase in the accuracy of the EP (unless over a long period of time) as well as making the actual plotting easier. The two ways of plotting are shown in Figs 3.8 and 3.9.

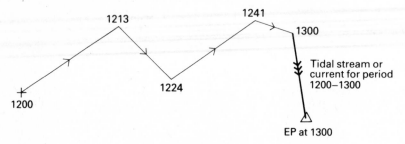

3.8 A good method of working up an EP with multiple courses

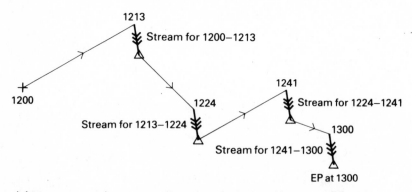

3.9 A less accurate and more complicated method of working up an EP with multiple courses

Working on small scale charts If the chart used for plotting is of a very small scale then while it might be of an adequate scale for overall strategy and other purposes, it is quite possible that the length of any one of the vectors going to make up an EP will be so short as to be insignificant on the chart, and very small plotting differences will become considerable in distance. In this case it can sometimes be better and more accurate to work up the plot since the last EP or fix to a larger scale, either on a separate plotting sheet or on a spare bit of the chart, and having obtained a resultant vector accurately, plotting this resultant on the chart.

Setting a Course

Calculating the course to steer from one place to another allowing for tidal streams and leeway is yet another familiar use of vector diagrams. Here you are making an intelligent guess as to what the boat speed and leeway angle are likely to be, calculating the tidal streams for the expected period of the passage, and putting them together (as in Fig. 3.10) while remembering that in this case you will have to reverse the sign of the leeway angle mentioned in Chapter 2 when doing step 5.

Step 1 Join starting position and destination with a 'track' line.

Step 2 Calculate the tidal stream vector(s) for the *approximate* duration of the passage and plot them using any convenient scale from the starting point.

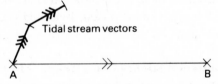

Step 3 Set dividers or drawing compasses to a length equal to the estimated distance though the water that will be covered during the period of the tidal stream vectors. This must be to the *same scale* as the tidal vectors. Strike an arc with this from the end of the tide line to where it crosses the track.

Step 4 Draw in the line joining these two points to get the course to steer (without leeway).

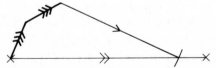

Step 5 If leeway needs to be taken into account, then *add* the estimated leeway angle if on starboard tack and *subtract* the angle if on port tack.

3.10 Setting or shaping a course to steer

If there are many hours of tidal stream to be taken into account, then the resultant of all the vectors can very often be found by adding together similar direction tidal streams. For example, in a cross-tide you may end up with a total of say 10.6 miles west-going stream and 16.8 miles east-going stream: in this case you would allow 6.2 miles of east-going stream in your shaping diagram (subtract the smaller figure from the larger and take the direction of the larger figure).

Obtaining and Using Tidal Stream Information

In order to be able to either shape courses or work up EPs one must of course be able to calculate the direction and rate of the tidal stream. Although knowledge of the sources of this information (tidal stream atlases, current tables and charts, etc) is assumed, there are some practical hints worth considering.

Timing of tidal stream information Probably one of the most common sources of error, albeit minor, is a misunderstanding of what period is meant by '5 hours before HW' or '2 hours after HW' in the tidal stream atlas or tidal diamond table. In fact, the time stated is always the *middle* of the hour that the data refers to, thus, for a HW time of 1147 the tidal stream given for '1 hour before HW' would be that for the period 1017 to 1117.

Interpolation between springs and neaps Most people who have used an Admiralty tidal stream atlas will have used the graph inside the front cover to interpolate between spring and neap tides for the rate on a particular day. However, I am sure that a lot of navigators do as I used to and interpolate arithmetically for the same purpose when using tidal diamonds, when of course the same graph can be used.

To simplify matters I have made up my own graph, with a large enough 'range' of tides down the side of the graph to cover all Standard Ports likely to be encountered, and with tidal stream rates of up to 10 knots along the graph, which should cater for most places. I then put the mean spring and neap ranges for the Standard Ports relevant to a particular race along the top of the graph ready for use with any chart in the race folio. This graph is reproduced in Appendix 1.

In areas covered by one of the *Stanford's Tidal Atlases* even this simple graph is not required as the interpolation figures are given on each page in tabular form. If you are regularly using charts based on one Standard Port, you can utilise the fact that the neap rate is very often (nearly always?) half of the spring rate to make up your own tables of rate against range for that port. In order to be able to extrapolate far enough above springs and below neaps will normally involve about 200–300 calculations. While this sounds tedious, it only takes about an hour per table with a pocket calculator. To assist navigators, particularly those on the South Coast of England, I have reproduced the tables that I use in Appendix 2.

Sometimes, a simplified form of arithmetic interpolation is useful rather than always relying on the graphical format – particularly for 'in the cockpit' calculations. For this purpose I always compare the ranges for the day (at the required place) with the mean spring and neap ranges to find a simple fractional difference, as in the example below; this fractional difference can then be applied to any mean tidal stream/current rates.

Example

Range today	4.6 m	(Between HW and LW)
Mean spring range	6.2 m	(From tide table
Mean neap range	1.5 m	or almanac)

(1) Difference MSR − MNR = 6.2 − 1.5 = 4.7
(2) Difference MSR − Range today = 6.2 − 4.6 = 1.6

Difference (2) compared to difference (1): $\dfrac{1.6}{4.7} = \dfrac{1}{3}$ approx.

∴ Range today = Springs − ⅓ (Difference)
∴ Rate today = Springs − ⅓ (Difference)

If mean spring rate is say 2.4 knots, and mean neap rate 1.5 knots (both obtained from tidal stream/current atlas or chart):

Difference = 2.4 − 1.5 = 0.9
∴ Rate today = 2.4 − (⅓ × 0.9) = 2.4 − 0.3 = 2.1 knots.

Since the fractional value can be worked out in the pre-race planning, this leaves merely the last few steps to be done during the race and they can normally be done as a mental calculation.

Plotting tidal vectors from an atlas When using tidal diamonds there is no choice as to the method of extracting the direction of the streams, as they are only given as a True bearing. However, with a tidal stream atlas there are several ways of taking the directional information and transferring it onto the chart. Undoubtedly the *least* accurate and the most time-consuming method is to convert the direction of the arrows in the atlas into a bearing and then plot this bearing on the chart. The way that I favour is to place the tidal stream atlas over the chart in the approximate position where the vector is needed, put a straightedge parallel to the appropriate tidal arrow, and then remove the atlas, leaving the straightedge on the chart still aligned properly. This is shown in Fig. 3.11 and although it sounds terribly inaccurate, in practice it is as accurate as any other method and quicker than most.

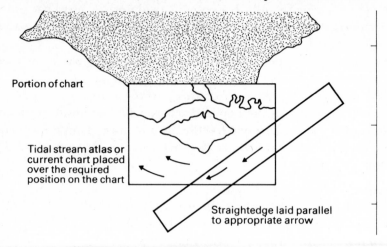

Portion of chart

Tidal stream atlas or
current chart placed
over the required
position on the chart

Straightedge laid parallel
to appropriate arrow

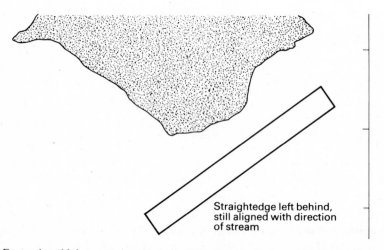

Straightedge left behind,
still aligned with direction
of stream

3.11 Extracting tidal stream (current) direction from a tidal stream atlas or chart.

Extracting data for several hours of tidal streams If you are coming to a turning mark where the next leg of the course is going to involve several hours' sailing in a cross-tide, then a simple and quick method of calculating the resultant of all the tidal vectors is required so that a course to steer can be worked out. In practice, the main problem is in extracting the basic information for each hour from the tidal atlas or chart in quick-reference form.

The basis of the method that I use is to have prepared beforehand several cards (file cards are ideal) marked along one edge with a likely boat speed, to the scale of the tidal stream atlas. Each card is marked with the boat speed it represents and the atlas that it is to be used with. Then, as soon as the approximate time of rounding the mark is known the cards for the most likely boat speeds for the upcoming leg are marked up with the tidal stream directions and rates for all the hours concerned, as in Fig. 3.12. The figures for stream rates obviously need to be corrected according to the tidal range, but the directions can just be marked on the card with arrows as this is normally accurate enough.

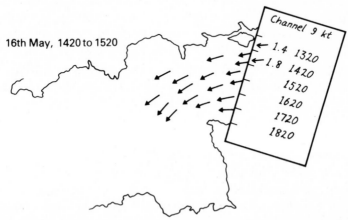

16th May, 1420 to 1520

Channel 9 kt

1.4 1320
1.8 1420
1520
1620
1720
1820

3.12 Transferring several hours' worth of information from a stream atlas onto a reference card. The edge of the card is laid along the anticipated rhumb-line course and on top of the tidal atlas pages for the period involved. Divisions on the card edge represent distance travelled in 1 hour at the boat speed on that card, and are to the latitude scale of the atlas. The arrows are accurate as to direction, but not speed which is listed numerically between the arrow and the time.

The next step is to add all the stream directions and rates together as already described so that the resultant is one, or at the most two, vectors; this resultant is then used as the amount of stream to allow for in setting the course. As the whole procedure can quite quickly be repeated for several different boat speeds, different courses to steer can be pre-calculated for these different speeds before the buoy is reached and thus the actual course to steer will be known as soon as the buoy is rounded.

Having worked through the tidal stream atlas in this manner for all likely boat speeds, working up EPs later is made very easy as the tidal stream vectors for each hour are already known.

Making a tidal stream atlas In areas which are not covered by a tidal stream atlas, obtaining tidal stream data can be a very time-consuming process, particularly if using a smallish scale passage chart, as one needs to go to large scale charts to get enough tidal diamonds or other data from the chart itself. It can be worth making your own tidal stream atlas from all the tidal stations available as part of the pre-planning for a race. With care this will be accurate, and as well as making subsequent tidal allowances easier, it might well show up trends in times of tide changes or even inshore eddies that would probably go unnoticed without being drawn out as in an atlas.

Using a Sextant

The sextant is merely an instrument for measuring angles very accurately. It can only do this effectively if it is looked after with some care, otherwise the accuracy of measurement will suffer dramatically. It is fairly obvious that the two mirrors have to be set up on at exactly the right angles in both the horizontal and vertical planes, and the initial adjustment of the sextant as per the manufacturer's instructions should remove virtually all the errors. Any error left after this adjustment is called the Index Error and has to be checked and allowed for every time the sextant is used. The way to check the index error is to set the sextant arm at approximately zero and then sight on either the horizon or a celestial body (Fig. 3.14). Turn the micrometer until the reflected image and the direct image exactly converge. The reading on the sextant at this time is the index error and must be subtracted from (added to, if the error is 'off the arc') any angles obtained. It is good practice to check for index error each time the sextant is used and before taking a sight as this will show up any knocks the instrument has sustained.

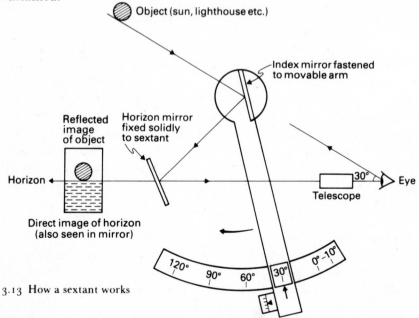

3.13 How a sextant works

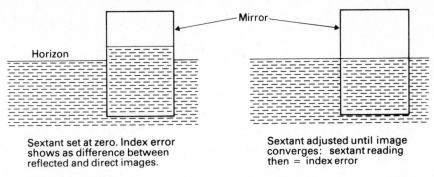

Sextant set at zero. Index error shows as difference between reflected and direct images.

Sextant adjusted until image converges: sextant reading then = index error

3.14 Finding the index error

The quickest way to ruin a sextant is to allow salt water to lie on the mirrors for any period of time. The salt will eat away at the protection of the mirror and eventually at the silvering itself. If any spray has landed on the sextant it is important to wash this off with fresh water as soon as possible. To avoid having to touch the mirrors an easy way to do this is to rinse the sextant in a bucket of fresh water and if possible to let it dry naturally before re-stowing it.

Taking a sight Whether taking a sight or obtaining a vertical angle for finding the 'distance off', the procedure is more or less the same. First a secure position is found with one's torso free to move to damp out the boat's gyrations but the lower part of the body wedged so that there is no need to hold on for balance. This position should be reasonably high to enable the horizon to be seen above as many waves as possible.

The index error is then obtained and noted. Having done this, set the sextant to approximately the right angle; the method of doing this varies with the type of sight being taken. With most sights the easiest method is to set the sextant to zero and look directly at the object. Then slowly and smoothly lower the sextant from this angle while its arm is moved to keep the object in the mirror all the time. When the sextant is about level with the horizon, the object should still be in the mirror and final adjustments of the arm can be made to obtain the exact angle. If taking a sun sight, be careful to use adequate shades for both the reflected and the direct image, to avoid damage to your eyes. If a vertical angle of an object on land is being obtained, the angle will normally be small enough so that this procedure is not necessary.

While the sextant is being finely adjusted to get the object resting just on the horizon, it is vital that it is kept absolutely vertical as large errors will otherwise develop. This can be checked by tilting the sextant gently from side to side, which will make the object appear to describe an arc (Fig. 3.15), and then taking the reading when it is at its lowest apparent position. If a celestial sight is being taken, then the precise time to the

45

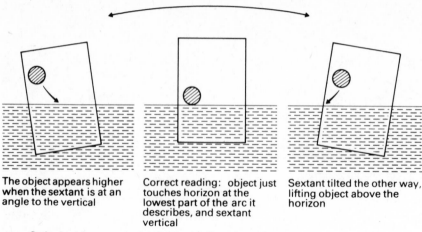

The object appears higher when the sextant is at an angle to the vertical

Correct reading: object just touches horizon at the lowest part of the arc it describes, and sextant vertical

Sextant tilted the other way, lifting object above the horizon

3.15 Swinging the sextant through a small arc by tilting it

second is needed, and the log reading is also recorded for working up the position later.

Sources of Position Lines

There are numerous ways of obtaining a position line (or LOP) and most of the important ones are looked at below. When using position lines to get a fix always remember that lines obtained by different methods can be mixed at will, and that three position lines are normally required for a fix, two to actually fix the position with the third to check the accuracy of the other two.

Transits One of the most accurate and simplest forms of position line, yet it is neglected by a lot of navigators. A transit can be formed by lining up *any* two fixed objects so long as they are positively identifiable. It is worthwhile studying the chart in the pre-planning stages of navigation in order to find likely transits, such as two headlands coming into line, an island and a beacon, markers for a measured distance, etc. These transits can then be used during the race as they come up and without any effort involved, to give a good position line. If an area is going to be raced over often, then one's own personal transits can be found by experience, to show the exact position of rocks, shallow water, etc (see Chapter 4).

Magnetic Bearings Position lines obtained with a hand bearing compass must be the most common, and so little needs to be said about them. It is worth remembering that bearings on near objects are more accurate than bearings taken on distant objects. Having taken magnetic bearings they can be plotted on the chart directly or they can be plotted as horizontal angles with the aid of a station pointer or piece of tracing paper. The advantages of direct plotting are that it is easy to do and any errors are likely to show up as a 'cocked hat', whereas with horizontal angle plotting, deviation on the bearings is obviated as shown in Fig. 3.16 but no indication of error is given.

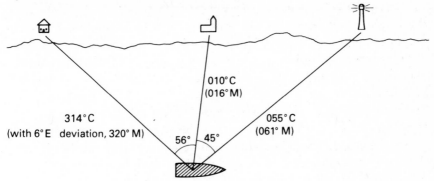

3.16 Horizontal angles obtained from compass bearings. As can be seen, the *angles* between the bearings stay the same regardless of deviation. Note that though *bearings* of only two objects give a fix, the single *angle* thus obtained does not have the same value as it can be at any point on a circle: thus two angles, provided by three objects, are required for a fix.

Horizontal sextant angles Although very accurate in theory, this type of position line is in practice so difficult to obtain under way as to be totally impracticable on the average sized yacht. As an alternative, compass bearings of the three marks should be taken instead.

Vertical sextant angles With practice, vertical sextant angles are one of the easiest and most accurate position line sources available. Fig. 3.17 shows the basic principle involved, and from there it is simple trigonometry to work out the distance off. In practice, having got the sextant angle it is easiest to either look the distance off in tables prepared for this purpose (found in most almanacs) or to use the formula:

$$\text{Distance (in miles)} = \frac{\text{Height (ft)} \times 0.565}{\text{Sextant angle (Minutes)}}$$

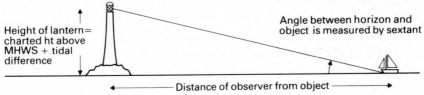

3.17 Vertical sextant angles

If a plastic sextant is used it can be worthwhile removing the telescope completely before attempting to get a vertical angle, particularly on murky days, as this gives a far clearer image and the additional accuracy obtainable with the telescope is not required.

Whether a tidal calculation is worthwhile to convert the height of the object from 'above MHWS' to 'above actual sea level' will depend on the comparative sizes of the likely tidal difference from MHWS and the height of the object. It will probably only be worth doing a tidal height calculation if the difference is likely to be greater than 5 per cent of the height of the object. In any case only an approximate calculation is required; certainly the Twelfths' Rule sort of accuracy would be adequate.

The object used can be a short distance inland, but any great distances will start to introduce errors as the apparent horizon will be in the wrong place. There are tables available (for example in Bowditch) will give the distance off from angles taken on distant objects such as mountains, but these use a totally different formula.

Celestial sights Position lines can also be obtained from the measurement of the angle between the horizon and most heavenly bodies. This subject is too complicated to be dealt with adequately here and is covered by other books. It is worth saying, though, that with a calculator to do the sums for you, anyone who can take a vertical sextant angle can also take a 'sight'. I use celestial sights quite often, even on medium length offshore races, as another aid to navigation.

Distance off by lights rising or dipping As the earth's curvature is known, if the height of an object such as a lighthouse is known along with the height of eye of the observer, then it is a fairly simple matter to calculate the distance at which the object will just dip (disappear) below the horizon. Once again, this is made even easier by tables that show the distance off for any height of light (from chart or Light List). So when a light can just be seen when standing on deck or when the boat is on the top of a wave, but it disappears below the *horizon* as the height of eye lessens, then its distance away can be looked up and so a position line plotted, which will be the arc of a circle centred on the light. This is not a very accurate method of obtaining position lines and errors up to about a mile are not uncommon. However, it is another source of approximate position lines that can be pre-planned before the race for the major lights, and at the distance off the coast that is likely at the time it is often accurate enough.

Radio bearings Essentially the same as bearings obtained from a hand bearing compass; see Chapters 2 and 7.

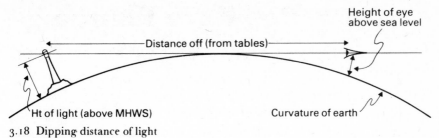

3.18 Dipping distance of light

Soundings In certain circumstances a fairly accurate position line can be obtained by using an echo-sounder. This is particularly valuable if it is known that the yacht is going to pass over a very much deeper or a much shallower patch of water such as a rocky ledge or a deep rift in the seabed. It can be possible to get an approximate position line with little effort, especially if the sounder has alarms that can be preset to show expected changes in depth. The traditionally described method of obtaining a position line from a whole series of soundings is far less useful: it takes too long to calculate the distances run between each sounding and even then the trace or line of soundings obtained very often can not be fitted to any charted soundings. However, in bad visibility this method of fixing can prove to be a life-saver, if the bottom topography is such as to be readily and unambiguously related to the line of soundings.

Clearing Bearing or Safe Distance Off

One use of a single position line that is often overlooked is in keeping clear of a danger. Rather than trying to keep a continuous fix of the position and seeing whether this is safe, which must be a retrospective action, it is often better to have a pre-planned line on the chart beyond which it is known or assumed to be *unsafe*. This line may be a bearing to be checked by hand bearing compass, or better still a transit. The latter is very easy to use as the transit can be seen to be closing while one is concentrating on other things.

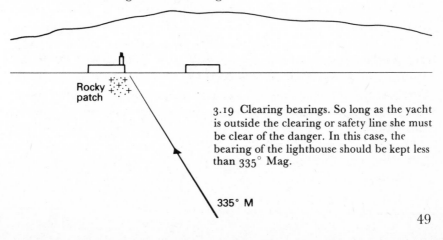

3.19 Clearing bearings. So long as the yacht is outside the clearing or safety line she must be clear of the danger. In this case, the bearing of the lighthouse should be kept less than 335° Mag.

Chapter 4 **Pre-Race Planning**

The navigator on a racing yacht has so many tasks to do during a race that any ways of taking work away from the busy race time and into the pre-race period must be valuable. A great deal of data can be extracted from various larger publications and put into more usable formats, and there is a lot of thinking that can best be done before the race. This chapter looks at which information can be extracted, how best to arrange and present data for use during the race, what decisions can be made (or at least thought about) beforehand, and what information can be obtained before the race that it would be impossible to get after the start.

'Floppy Files'

I have found that the soft-backed books of polythene sleeves or envelopes obtainable from office stationers are the most convenient way to hold sheets of data for use afloat. If the tops of the envelopes are sealed with tape they are reasonably waterproof but it is still a simple matter to change a sheet when necessary. Writing on the envelopes of data can be done with a Chinagraph pencil or a felt-tip pen of the type used for overhead projector transparencies. A waterproof marker can be cleaned off afterwards with a solvent such as acetone.

In my own navigation I use three or four of these files at any one time, some of them to hold permanent information and some for data that is specific to a particular race or yacht.

File 1 – Tidal stream atlases The larger versions of these floppy files normally have room for about 40 sheets and thus can hold three tidal stream atlases. Putting the atlases in folders has the advantage that they last a lot longer as they are less likely to get soggy, as well as keeping all the tidal stream information together. If the final page of the folder contains an interpolation graph with a large enough range, it can be used for interpolation between springs and neaps for all the atlases. Interpolation tables like those in Appendix 2 can also be included to make life even easier.

Obviously each tidal atlas page should be marked with the time that it will represent during the period of that particular race.

File 2 – General information Exactly what goes into this file will depend on your own particular needs, but as a guideline, any table or data sheet which you use on a regular basis should be included, as must an index of the contents. The latter is particularly important if other crew members might use the folder. The following are the major items that I feel should be included.

INDEX

CHART LIST should include the consecutive number of the chart within the folio, the chart number, its title and scale. Ideally the charts will be arranged in a separate folio for each race so that only those necessary are taken. This has several advantages in addition to the fact that the charts last longer. First, if all the charts are taken ashore after each race then there is more likelihood of their being corrected up to date for the next race than if they are left on board between races. Second, they can be put into logical order for the next race, re-numbered sequentially, and a new chart list made with only the charts that will be needed.

Particularly in unfamiliar areas, it is also worth supplementing the written chart list with a diagram showing the boundaries of each chart. This sort of key facilitates choosing the most sensible chart in any given circumstance, whereas merely having the list may mean that an un-suitably scaled chart is used by mistake or time wasted finding the one you really want.

RADIO BEACONS Almanacs, radio signals lists, radio beacon charts and so on usually cover a much larger area than that required for a particu-lar race or even for a series, except for some ocean races. It will therefore save effort during the race to copy the information on call signs, frequencies, ranges, etc for all potentially useful beacons onto a single sheet; this can show the aerobeacons as well as the marine ones, and the sequences of beacons in their chains. Incidentally, it is also worth ensuring that all the relevant radiobeacons are actually marked on all the charts which might be used and that their positions are up to date. To ensure this, in British coastal waters have a copy of the Admiralty publication NP280 *Radio Services for Small Craft*, ashore for this planning. Changes to radio navigation aids are published in Notices to Mariners.

VERTICAL SEXTANT ANGLE TABLES Although these are in most almanacs it is much easier to look them up on 'page 4' of your own file than on 'page 247' of an almanac. What I do is cut out the relevant pages from an out-of-date almanac and put them in the floppy file.

DISTANCE OFF RISING DIPPING This table can also be taken from an old almanac. However, as one's height of eye on a yacht is always going to be within a very limited range it is probably worth the effort of extracting the relevant columns from the table.

TIDAL STREAM INTERPOLATION TABLES may be put into this file or, as discussed above, placed with the tidal stream atlases.

COMPASS DEVIATION CURVES It is assumed that the compasses on the yacht will have been swung, and corrected as accurately as possible, but if any error is left then obviously a deviation curve will be required. If the errors are small enough not to be important very often, then a floppy file is probably a good place for them. If the residual errors are large enough to warrant being taken into account all the time, then it is better to stick the curves up where they can be easily seen.

RDF ERROR CURVE As discussed in Chapter 7, the RDF set will be subject to both deviation errors on its compass and to quadrantral errors in receiving the radio waves. Once a position in the boat where these errors are at a minimum has been found, a curve can be plotted of both; once again the floppy file is a convenient place for this, preferably next to the radio beacon information.

DOWNWIND TACKING ANGLE TABLE Invaluable, particularly when speed polar diagrams are not available (see Appendix 3).

SAIL CHANGE POLAR DIAGRAM Constructing such a diagram is covered in Chapter 5; suffice to say here that it is an important data sheet which should if at all possible be prepared for every seriously raced yacht. If sailing on an unfamiliar yacht which does not have such a polar diagram, it can be worth using one from another yacht with similar sails in its wardrobe as the apparent wind angles for each sail change are likely to be similar. It is also much easier to modify an existing polar diagram to suit the individual yacht than to prepare one from scratch.

SPEED POLAR CURVES Also discussed in Chapter 5. They should be included in the data file whenever possible.

WEATHER FORECASTS As the times and frequencies of weather forecasts are designed for the broadcasters and not to make them easy to remember, I find it useful to obtain these facts from almanacs, newspapers, etc and write them down in two different ways, first chronologically starting at midnight and secondly station by station.

File 3 – Specific race information Most of this file needs to be made up anew for each race, or in some cases for each race series. Once again the exact content of this file is a matter of personal choice, but the list below gives an idea of the sort of things which should be included.

TIDE TIMES AND HEIGHTS For each Standard Port that may possibly be used during a race (found by looking at the charts for the race to see which port is used for tidal stream data and at the course for likely tidal heights that might be needed). I extract from the tide tables the times and heights of high and low water for the likely duration of the race, which eliminates having to look them up during the race with the attendent risk of using the wrong month, time zone etc. Together with this information I record the mean ranges for springs and neaps, and where possible include the tidal curve for the port (taken from an out-of-date tide table). Appendix 1 gives an actual example of the tidal data which I recorded for one particular race.

TIDAL HEIGHTS Having extracted the high and low water data, I then take my pre-planning one stage further. If there are specific points during the race where it is likely that the height of tide above chart datum is going to be required (for example at the start, at any head-lands that are going to be approached, in fact at any time when the yacht is likely to be close to land) then I will estimate at what time 'my yacht' is going to arrive there and calculate the heights above datum for a few hours either side of this estimated time. This is also exemplified in Appendix 5 where it can be seen that the number of calculations necessary is probably around one or two hundred. With organization and a calculator, it only takes about half an hour to do.

If done with care this preparation should mean that *no* tidal height calculations at all need to be done during the race, thus saving time and energy for more immediate tasks.

TIDAL STREAMS AND TIDAL GATES As well as marking up the tidal stream atlases for each hour of the likely duration of the race, it is worth making a list in note form of when the tidal stream changes direction/rate significantly. It is particularly important to note any counter-currents or eddies and the times that the tide changes at headlands, etc in case of tidal 'gates' that may make it impossible to get around a headland or through a narrow channel against a foul tide.

RACE INSTRUCTIONS Having thoroughly read and inwardly digested the race instructions I then put a mark in the margin to draw attention to any peculiar items. Once this is done I transfer the document into a floppy file so that they don't get lost at the bottom of the chart table or end up as a soggy heap in the bilges.

COURSE This is the most crucial part of the race instructions and so as soon as it is known I write it down on a separate piece of paper along with the definitions of the start and finish lines and which side to round the marks. It can be worth having someone else check that this is correct in every respect, to avoid worry later.

MAJOR LIGHTS, LANDMARKS AND BUOYS A list of the characteristics of all of these in the approximate order that they might be sighted means that there is less chance of misidentifying them during the race. If one is careful to extract the data from the most up-to-date and informative source, be this the *List of Lights*, largest scale chart or whatever, then it also provides a check on the accuracy of the smaller scale charts which might well be used during the race.

WEATHER FORECASTS A floppy file is also a convenient place to store weather forecast forms and synoptic charts after they have been filled in: it gives an easy-to-use reference on the weather pattern over the whole period of the race. Meteorological charts or copies of television weather maps obtained before the race can also be included in this part of the file. Keeping forecast sheets neatly in this way also provides a record of the actual weather experienced during a race for later analysis of whether one's own interpretation of the weather patterns was correct.

It may not always be considered essential to collate all the information into files as has been suggested above, but this or a similar method of presentation will certainly make your job of navigating an awful lot easier and quicker, and also reduce the ever-present chance of errors.

Local Knowledge

Some navigators appear to have local knowledge while others still don't know their own area properly even after years of sailing on the same patch. Basically, this is usually because some people are prepared to go to the effort of writing down and cataloguing the information obtained after each race for later use, while others can't be bothered and treat each race as a totally separate happening. Mental notes are obviously the easiest to take at the time, and can be very impressive later in showing off one's knowledge. However, it is written notes that will be longer lasting and ultimately more reliable.

If you go aground in places where you thought you wouldn't, take note of this at the time and if possible get a couple of bearings or transits so that the exact spot can be looked at on the chart later. If the time of a grounding is also noted then it will also be possible to calculate the charted depth of water for future use.

When a counter-current or back eddy is experienced, then don't just note that fact: also take note of the time and the strength of the counter-current so that this can be related to the High Water time for the day and a picture of when the counter-current starts and finishes can gradually be built up. Eventually you might be able to produce your own local tidal stream atlas, showing all the counter-currents and when they are likely to happen.

If a particular stretch of coastline is going to be sailed along time after time, especially if it is rocky then it will be well worth the effort of going out at very low water in a motor boat or dinghy and studying exactly where the rocks are in relation to shore marks. This information can be written down in the form of pilotage notes, or even better it can be accurately plotted using very large scale charts or topographical maps (for example 1 : 2500 Ordnance Survey maps). This is obviously very time-consuming, but as a one-off exercise, perhaps during a winter or an 'off' year, it can pay handsome dividends in the long run. Bearings from the shore can sometimes be taken too, perhaps with less discomfort in midwinter!

Taking the above concept one stage further, it is possible to combine the detailed chart produced from this research with overlapping photographs of the shoreline from a few hundred feet off, to give both a plan and a sectional view. If the photographs are photocopied to the same scale as the chart, with rocks and prominent landmarks ringed, then a strip map of the area combining both can be made.

Sea breezes and other local wind effects can also be learned about over a period of a few years (months?). If the details of any such systems are written down whenever they happen, then patterns will gradually emerge as to their timing and they can then be predicted with more accuracy.

Armed with all this data on the local conditions, you gradually become more and more valuable to visiting yachts as navigator. The only danger with local knowledge is when it is extrapolated into unknown areas, perhaps with more 'dangerous' results than not using any local knowledge at all.

Just Before the Start

Most of the pre-race planning that we have looked at so far can be done days or weeks before a race, or sometimes even during the previous winter. However, some planning cannot be carried out until just before the start: this normally relates mainly to the weather, the start line and sometimes to the course, particularly on shorter races.

Obviously an up-to-the-minute weather *forecast* should be obtained as late as possible before the start, ideally by phone from an actual meteorologist. In the British Isles you can obtain this type of forecast from either a local weather centre, the meteorological office in Bracknell, or from a local airport. It can be supplemented *before* the start by a telephone or radio call to Coastguard stations to get local weather *reports* along the course.

As discussed in Chapter 9 on strategy, once the start line is known its bias relative to the wind must be found as must the tidal stream bias in the immediate vicinity of the start. The apparent wind on the first leg needs to be calculated or found by experiment, and wind shifts must be noted to try to establish any pattern that there might be.

If the course is not already known from the race instructions then it will normally be given at either the five or the ten minute signal and this leaves very little time before the start to work out any changes in strategy for the first leg. If the course is given just prior to the start in this manner, then it is *always* worth having someone else in the crew check that no mistake has been made in writing it down – and incidentally, always write it down, never try to remember it even if it is a simple-sounding course or code. Some very important races have been lost by mis-remembering which buoy comes next or which way round to leave a mark.

Self-preparation There are two aspects to one's own preparation, mental and physical. Mentally, it is important that you, as navigator, feel that you have done as much as possible before the race so that you know that you are as ready as possible before the start. Physically, it is important to be as rested as you can, not to have a hangover and to be comfortable in all respects. This means having a good night's sleep the day before a big race, not showing the foredeck crew how to drink the evening before, and having eaten a sensible meal (especially if you are prone to seasickness), taken seasick pills if required and been to the loo, all before the ten minute gun.

Chapter 5 **Performance Data Analysis**

One of the tasks which normally falls upon the shoulders of the regular navigator is that of data recording and analysis for the purpose of tuning. This data collection is vital for a successful campaign as, first, it enables fast combinations of sails to be set up again, and second, it can give the navigator actual figures to work on when deciding which of a number of strategic options to take in a specific situation. The amount of time and effort that is put into obtaining data and its subsequent analysis will depend on how serious the yacht's campaign is and on the facilities available for data collection. The work can range from simply recording the wind strengths and sheet lead positions for the various genoas, to preparing detailed performance records using polar diagrams of one type or another for specific sails and wind speeds. This chapter is on the more extensive kind of analysis and it is up to the crew and individuals to decide on how much they are prepared to do.

What Information is Required?

Before one can even start to look at methods of data collection and analysis, it is necessary to decide exactly what information is going to be needed during a race. There are two distinct sides to the information required.

TUNING DATA In any given wind strength and direction there will be a particular combination of sails which gives the best speed. Therefore one important aspect of data collection is the recording of good (and bad) sail combinations together with as many relevant details of sheeting positions, halyard tensions and so on as possible. This will enable the good combinations to be repeated in the same conditions at a later date while avoiding slow combinations.

STRATEGICALLY IMPORTANT DATA As well as needing to know which sails to hoist, it is very important for the navigator to know what the speed of the yacht will be once they have been set so that the correct strategy can be employed without resorting to guesswork.

Obviously these two aspects of data analysis are inextricably linked, it being impossible to predict the boat speed unless it is also possible to decide on the right sails for the conditions. However, as we shall see later it is more convenient to separate the two different aspects of data for a simple-to-use presentation.

Data Collection

Actually obtaining the data for subsequent analysis is a fairly lengthy and mundane process. Before any reliable information can be analysed, it is necessary to collect literally thousands of individual pieces of data and unless one is very well organized this will probably prove to be too large a task for most people.

Repetition of tension settings Before it is possible to record any information on sheet lead positions, halyard tensions, etc it is necessary to mark all the possible positions in some way so that it is possible to set up a sail in the same way again. Halyards should be marked for block-to-block positions and also for an approximate tension for each sail. These marks can be a piece of sticky tape, paint, coloured ink or a seizing (with coloured whipping twine?) around the line or wire. Having marked the actual control line it is then necessary to put a corresponding mark on the deck or mast. Sticky tape with numbers printed on it at set distances can be obtained for this purpose. An example of the markings needed on a halyard can be seen in Fig. 5.1.

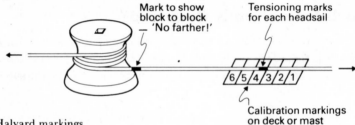

5.1 Halyard markings

Sheet lead positions need to be marked as well, ideally with a unique marking for each position to avoid confusion. The usual way to mark genoa sheeting positions is to stamp the track with numbers at each hole, thus enabling the carriage to be reset easily to a predetermined place. If several tracks are used to alter the sheeting angle, then either each track needs to be 'named' (forward/inner, forward/middle, etc) or else every hole should have its own number, starting at 1 and going up to the total number of possible positions on that side of the deck. It is not a good practice to start each track at number 1 as this can lead to mistakes being made as to which tracks should be used.

In some circumstances it may be better to allow only a few set positions on a control line (tight, medium, loose?) rather than allowing infinitely fine control and for this balls swaged onto a wire with a key-hole plate in lieu of a normal cleat can be a good idea on smaller boats. Particularly in the sort of situation where Barber hauling in more than one direction is possible, it may be so complicated with an 'analogue' (infinitely variable) system of controls that the same result may be impossible to obtain a second time. Beware, though, of using this type of control where the loadings are going to be severe: it may prove impossible to move the control lines under load!

Hydraulic systems lend themselves admirably to repetition of setting as one nearly always has a pressure gauge to measure tension. At present, though, these are normally limited to such functions as back-stay, vang, babystay, etc even on large yachts as they do not give the range of adjustment needed for such things as genoa sheets. I have sailed in one yacht where the final mainsheet tension was by a hydraulic ram and this certainly allowed the mainsail leech tension to be set up predictably.

Whatever method of calibration is used, the important thing is being able to reproduce the same tensions and results, and repeat combinations which are known to be good. As the sails get older and their material stretches, however slightly, the *exact* shape will not necessarily be reproduced by setting halyards etc to the same tensions. However, a previously set up position which was known to be good is still obviously better than trial and error each time, and the precise setting of controls can be changed when it is *seen* to be necessary; the new settings for the best shape should then be recorded.

Recording the data If data is to be recorded for both tuning and strategic purposes, then a large number of wind headings are required and so a form is needed to ensure that the correct and complete data is recorded and to make subsequent analysis easier by presenting the data in the same way each time. It may be worth having separate forms for upwind and downwind work as the data to be recorded is somewhat different for each. Fig. 5.2 shows suitable headings, which can be prepared as proformas.

		RACE/PRACTICE _____ DATE _____ YACHT _____								
TIME	AVE. SPEED	APP. WIND		WAVES		HEEL	VANG	BACK STAY	BABY STAY	MAINSAIL	HEADSAILS/SPIN.	REMARKS
		ANGLE	SPEED	HT	DIR.					REEFS/SHEET/ETC.	WHICH/SHEETING	

5.2 Tuning data form

During an actual race it may well not be feasible to spend time writing all this data down, since one's function as navigator is then to help in winning that race. This will depend on the importance of the race being sailed at the time compared to the need for accurate data for future races. As a general rule, if the race in hand is an important one then only the most important or new data should be bothered with, whereas if this race is merely a work-up towards a more important series then it is probably worthwhile expending a fair bit of effort in obtaining information for use later, even at the expense of possibly losing a place or two. It takes quite strong discipline to work towards better long-term results in what are effectively practice races, but it is an important part of working up an offshore racer – experiment when it doesn't matter and record the results, and then play safe during the important races using the results of earlier experiments and only experimenting further when a previously unknown set of circumstances arises.

If a yacht's campaign is serious enough for the navigator to go to the bother of attempting to record all this data, then it should also be important enough to the rest of the crew to spend some time while not racing just trying out different combinations of sails and trimming in a wide variety of conditions. This sort of genuine practice is invaluable for data collection as it makes it possible to evaluate the boat speed over a large number of wind angles fairly quickly. In order to obtain sufficient data to make sail potential curves, and to calculate the optimum pointing angles with each sail upwind, it is necessary to try the genoas with all the different reefing possibilities and at relative angles to the wind between 'pinching' and 'full and by' – if possible by changing the angle to the wind by a single degree at a time. Obviously it will only be possible to evaluate one or two genoas at any one practice session unless the conditions are very varied. When practicing like this it is obviously vital that in each situation the boat is set up for the conditions with as much care as would be taken if it were a race. It is also important to allow the yacht (and crew) sufficient time after each change to settle down and then take a number of readings over a period of three or four minutes. Off the wind, such exactitude is only necessary near a dead run or at other points where a significant jump or fall in speed is found to occur with a small change in apparent wind angle, for example the point where a yacht just starts to plane or surf. In most cases it is sufficient to record boat speed, etc at 5° or even 10° steps.

Whether it is upwind or down, the most important points which must be determined in detail are where any performance change is about to happen, since it is the exact point at which a sail change needs to be carried out, or the conditions when it is worth bearing away by a few degrees, that is wanted in the end. It is therefore not so important to have detailed information on the situations when no significant change is about to happen.

Presentation of Information

Polar diagrams of one sort or another are the normal way to present the results of all this data analysis, and there are four basic kinds of polar diagram.

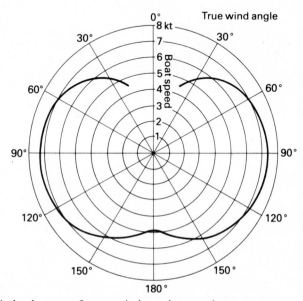

5.3 True wind polar curve for one wind speed, say 10 knots

True wind polar diagram The most difficult of all polar diagrams to make but potentially also one of the most useful ways of evaluating performance. Basically, all it does is relate boat speed to the angle of the *true wind* for a particular wind speed. This means that from the strategic point of view, knowing the true wind speed one could predict fairly accurately what the boat speed would be at any angle to the wind and thus as navigator one would be able to use this to plan the best course to steer.

To make a true wind polar diagram it is necessary to take the raw data relating to boat speed, apparent wind angle, apparent wind strength and so on and then reduce all the wind information into true wind. This means taking into account the boat speed, angle of heel, instrument errors, leeway angle, etc for every item of data. In a Twelve Metre campaign it is quite normal to have automatic recording of the readings of all the various instruments onto magnetic tape for later computer analysis. However, as we have seen, on a more normal yacht the data will be recorded by hand on paper and therefore the number of calculations required for a true wind polar diagram becomes phenomenally time-consuming. The type of programmable calculator discussed in Chapter 6 enables these calculations to be carried out somewhat faster but it is doubtful to me whether the effort involved is worthwhile.

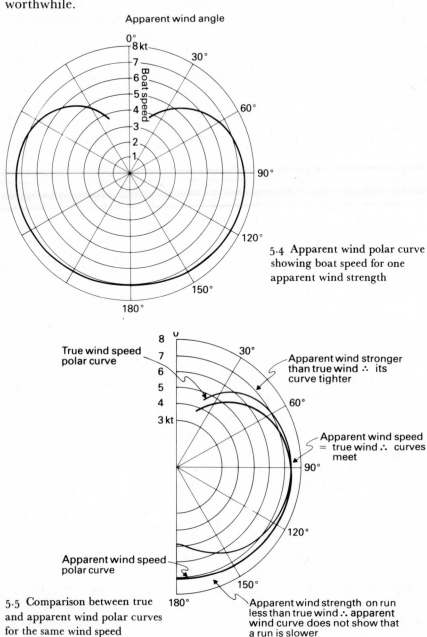

5.4 Apparent wind polar curve showing boat speed for one apparent wind strength

5.5 Comparison between true and apparent wind polar curves for the same wind speed

Fig. 5.3 shows a typical true wind polar diagram for an IOR yacht for one wind speed. To be useful in practice, at least three or four of these would have to be made, each for a different wind speed range.

Apparent wind polar diagram An apparent wind polar diagram (Fig. 5.4) relates boat speed to the apparent wind angle for a particular apparent wind velocity. This makes it a far easier diagram to construct than the true wind polar diagram as the data can be used more or less in its raw state, by merely plotting it as observed for a particular indicated wind strength, on graph paper. However it is not an easy job, since the apparent wind speed alters as the boat turns through various headings and a great deal of data has to be acquired to build up the whole curve.

Unfortunately it is not quite such a useful diagram to have as was the true wind diagram because it relates to the apparent wind strength which obviously changes as the heading changes. This means that, in practice, every time the apparent wind polar diagram is used for working out the expected boat speed on a different heading, the calculation to find the new apparent wind has to be done (see Chapter 8). Once again, with a good hand-held programmable calculator this is not too difficult, but it does limit the effective use of the apparent wind polar diagram.

Fig. 5.4 shows a typical apparent wind polar diagram while Fig. 5.5 shows the differences between a true wind and an apparent wind curve.

Sail potential curve A sail potential curve as shown in Fig. 5.6 is only an intermediate presentation of data. It shows how fast a particular sail or combination of sails is for different angles to the wind for one particular apparent wind strength.

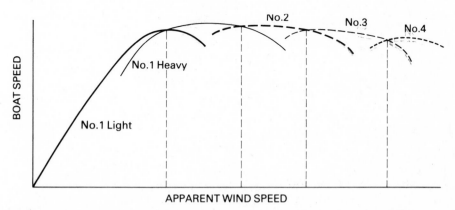

5.6a Upwind sail potential curves. Crossover points indicate ideal time to change from one genoa to the next.

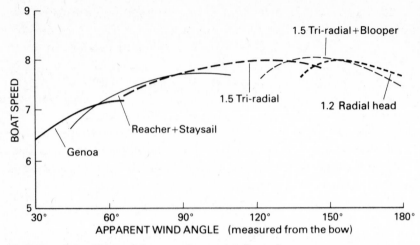

5.6b Downwind sail potential curves, for one wind speed

Once sail potential curves have been produced for all the possible combinations of sails in all the varying conditions, this data can be transferred to a sail change table.

Sail change table This is obtained from the sail potential curves. I have found it best to have two tables, one for upwind sails and another for offwind combinations (Figs. 5.7 and 5.8).

APPARENT WIND kts	GENOA	SHEET LEAD	MAINSAIL	BACKSTAY TENSION
0 – 8	No. 1 LIGHT	46	ALL CONTROLS EASED UP TO 5 OUTHAUL ON 5-8	1000 – 1500
6 – 14	No. 1 MEDIUM	44	CUNNINGHAM AT 10 FLATTENING REEF AT 12	1500 – 2500
12 – 19	No. 1 HEAVY	45	CUNNINGHAM + FLATTENER 1st REEF AT 17	2500 – 3500
17 – 24	No. 2	38	CUNNINGHAM + FLATTENER 1st REEF AT 21	3500 – 4000
22 – 32	No. 3	24	CUNNINGHAM + FLATTENER 1st REEF AT 24 2nd REEF AT 28	4000 .
30 – ?	No. 4	24	1st REEF 30 – 33 2nd REEF 33 – 39 3rd REEF 39 – ?	4000 EASE TO 3000

5.7 An upwind sail change table

APPARENT WIND kts	APPARENT WIND ANGLE (FROM BOW)															
	30°	40°	50°	60°	70°	80°	90°	100°	110°	120°	130°	140°	150°	160°	170°	180°
0 – 5	LIGHT No.1 or DRIFTER				0.5 oz RADIAL HEAD FLOATER							TOO SLOW !				
5 – 8	LIGHT No.1	JIB		0.75 oz TRI–RADIAL				0.5 oz FLOATER						ALWAYS TACK		
8 – 12	MEDIUM No.1 or HEAVY	JIB + REEFED STAYSAIL		0.75 oz TRI–RADIAL						0.75 oz up to 10 kt 1.2 oz RUNNER 10–12 kt				DOWNWIND		
				+ FULL–HOIST STAYSAIL									1.2 oz RUNNER			
12 – 18	HEAVY No.1			1.5 oz TRI–RADIAL						+ BLOOPER						
18 – 25	No.2 FULL MAIN	BLAST REACHER + REEFED STAYS'L				2.2 oz TRI–RADIAL				1.5 oz TRI–RADIAL						
25 – 30	No.3 1st REEF ?	BLAST REACHER					2.2 oz TRI–RADIAL				BLOOPER ?					
30 – ?	No.4 1 or 2 REEFS	No.3 + FULL MAIN			No.2 + FULL MAIN				2.2 oz TRI–RADIAL or HEAVY No.1 AS SPINNAKER							

5.8 A typical downwind sail change table

To summarize on polar diagrams, I would suggest that a sail change table is essential and that it is worthwhile expending some effort on obtaining data for an apparent wind polar curve especially for areas (relative to wind direction or wind strength) where small angular changes in heading are found to make large speed differences. For most people it is not worth the effort to attempt to make true wind polar curves, and it is doubtful whether it is worth making full sail potential curves.

Chapter 6 **Calculators**

Since the advent of the silicon chip, hand-held calculators have become a reality whether one likes them or not. It is now possible to buy over the counter calculators with the same power and capacity that mainframe computers of a decade ago used to have. For the racing yacht navigator these powerful programmable calculators offer a wide range of facilities, mainly to remove the drudgery from navigation but also to make possible some things that could not even be considered without the speed of a computer. Having used calculators of one sort or another to help me navigate for the last few years, I am certain that every racing navigator should have at least a basic calculator.

What are Calculators Capable of Doing?

In very basic terms, any time you use numbers or angles whether on a chart, in a notebook or from a table, it is possible to use a calculator to do the calculations for you. In theory, it would be possible to do away with plotting vector triangles, or looking numbers up in tables, and other manipulations altogether and replace them with button pushing, and this is what some people try to do. In practice, though, it is very often easier and quicker to draw a simple vector triangle or to look up a single number in a table which you have ready to hand than it would be to make 20 or 30 keying operations without a mistake. I feel very strongly that calculators should only be used for problems they actually make easier, and that there is no point whatsoever in inventing tasks for them. The following list, although by no means comprehensive, gives an idea of the areas of yacht navigation where a calculator of the right type can really be of assistance.

CALCULATING THE NEW APPARENT WIND AFTER THE NEXT MARK Although this is merely an application of vector triangles, it involves three separate triangles (true wind, new course to steer, and new apparent wind) and therefore does take time to draw. With a suitably programmed calculator it is definitely quicker to input the data, push the buttons and get out the answers.

66

TIDAL HEIGHT CALCULATIONS One area where even a relatively simple calculator can be used to advantage, especially in pre-planning. As we saw in Chapter 4, it is worthwhile working out the predicted heights of tide for strategic places along the course, and as the exact time of arrival at these places cannot be known this involves calculating the heights for several hours at each place. If the Admiralty tide tables are being used for these calculations, one is extracting factors from the tidal curves, multiplying these by the range, and adding the Low Water value to obtain the heights above datum. The calculator can be programmed to require just one input, the factor, for each calculation, using the equation:

Factor (put in each time) × Range (put in once as a constant)
+ LW height (put in as a second constant)
= Height above chart datum

With some of the more sophisticated calculators it is also possible to use the harmonic constant method of tidal prediction to give an hourly plot of the tidal height.

CELESTIAL OR ASTRO NAV Suitable calculators can greatly reduce the time it takes to work out a sun, moon or star sight, doing at least the work of the Air Navigation Tables' and in some cases working out the Nautical Almanac data as well. This facility makes astro nav feasible even on a busy racing yacht, and means that little or no theory is needed to be able to reduce a sight. Beware, though: with no knowledge of the basic principle being applied, errors can occur without you noticing them.

CALCULATING CORRECTED TIMES It is sometimes nice to be able to time competitors around marks and work out their corrected times to compare with your own, and a programmable calculator makes this job very easy. With a calculator which can convert hours, minutes and seconds into decimal hours and then work in these units, it is simple to write a program which has the start time of the race as a constant and which then takes the time of rounding (in 24 hours notation) and the TMF of the yacht, calculates the elapsed time, multiplies this by the TMF, and gives the corrected time (normally easiest to comprehend in hours, minutes and seconds). It is even possible to input the TMFs of all the yachts in the race as data before the race, label each piece of data (e.g. 1, 2, 3, etc) and then just have to punch in the time of rounding and the 'number' of the yacht rather than having to input her TMF each time.

Under IOR Rules, yachts race under a time-on-time handicapping system (under some rules time-on-distance is used). In order to calculate the corrected time of a yacht at any given moment it is first necessary to work out her TMF (time multiplying factor) from her rating, and the age allowance if any. The TMF is obtained by the formula:

$$TMF = \frac{a\sqrt{R}}{1 + b\sqrt{R}}$$

where: rating 23–70 ft a = 0.2424

b = 0.0567

under 23 ft a = 0.4039

b = 0.2337

An age allowance of 0.2% of TMF per year to a maximum of 4.4% can then be deducted from the TMF for yachts which are four years old or more.

The corrected time is then calculated as:

$$\text{Corrected Time} = \text{Elapsed Time} \times TMF$$

This would obviously be done each time it was considered worthwhile to get an idea of one's position during a race or immediately after finishing, but with a little more pre-planning most of the calculation can be done before the race. I always try to get a list of entries as early as possible and then work out the corrected time for each yacht after one hour of racing. Then taking your own yacht as the standard, the differences in corrected time for each hour of racing can be simply worked out, as in the example here:

Yacht	Rating	TMF	Corr. time (hr) (TMF × 3600)	Difference from *Caiman* (secs ±)
Caiman II	32.8	1.0480	3772.8	—
Formidable	34.4	1.0669	3840.8	±68.0
Intuition	31.9	0.0370	3733.2	−39.6

It is then straightforward to multiply the difference per hour by the number of hours/part hours raced to see how much ahead or behind in time a particular yacht *should* be and therefore to see who is winning at that time. At the end of the race it is obviously worthwhile working out your own corrected time accurately and also the times of your nearest rivals.

Corrected times lend themselves admirably to fully programmable calculators, especially if the TMFs of all the competing yachts can be held on a data card to be used whenever needed.

DISTANCE OFF CALCULATIONS Simple Distance off by Vertical Sextant Angle is probably easiest to obtain from a table, but if the distance off from an object whose base is below the horizon is wanted, then a calculator can be of assistance. The formula for finding the distance is:

$$\text{Distance} = \sqrt{\left(\frac{\tan \text{ (sextant alt.)}}{0.000246}\right)^2 + \frac{\text{Height of object (ft)} - \text{Ht of eye}}{0.74736}}$$

$$- \frac{\tan \text{ (sextant alt.)}}{0.000246}$$

When using this formula it must be borne in mind that the distance off will not necessarily be accurate due to refraction, but where there is high ground relatively close to the sea it can be a useful guide at least.

LINEAR REGRESSION When taking a fix or a sight, it is normal to check each bearing or angle two or three times and then to 'average out' the results before plotting them. While this is obviously more accurate than just taking one attempt at each, an arithmetic average will not necessarily give the most accurate result. There is a statistical procedure called linear regression which can be used to analyse this type of result, discard any spurious readings and give an 'average' of the good readings. Most programmable calculators have this facility.

The use of scientific and programmable calculators in solving a wide range of problems is the subject of a book entitled *Practical Navigation by Calculator* by Gerry Keys (pub. Stanford Maritime).

Calculator Types

To simplify matters somewhat, it can be considered here that there are four basic types of calculator available at present.

SIMPLE ARITHMETIC MACHINES Such calculators cost very little and even the simplest ones can add, subtract, multiply and divide quickly and accurately. For navigation, the use of arithmetic machines is obviously very limited but if no other type is available at least it will do the necessary multiplication and division for you.

SLIDE-RULE (SCIENTIFIC) CALCULATORS Although most scientific calculators have a host of functions, they are hardly any more worthwhile than the simplest type. In order to utilise their functions too much keying has to be done, in my opinion, when they have no programmable capability: thus it is normally easier to plot the vectors or look up the data in tables.

PROGRAMMABLE AND ADVANCED PROGRAMMABLE CALCULATORS As soon as you can put a series of key strokes into a calculator as a program for it to execute later (and as often as you wish) then calculators really can help. All the navigation applications discussed in this chapter need a programmable machine. For even a programmable type to be really useful, it must be possible to re-use the programs without having to key them in each time it is turned on, and this means that the calculator must have either a permanent memory which holds the programs in store even when switched off or magnetic cards or something similar to store the programs on. If you are interested in using a calculator to the full, an advanced programmable with a card reader is definitely the way to go. The machines which are currently available are suitable (spring 1982) are, in my order of preference, Hewlett Packard HP 41C, Texas Instruments TI 59, Hewlett Packard HP 67 and Casio FX 502P.

'DEDICATED' CALCULATORS For the non-technically minded, there are a few calculators available which have built-in programs to do basic navigation functions. These are especially good for doing celestial navigation but are not so suitable for racing oriented programs. Plath make one superb calculator if you have the money for it, but at a more realistic level is the Tamaya NC 77 which is a very well made machine with all the astro nav functions you could want. This is about the same price as the TI 59 or HP 67, but is far more limited as it is not programmable and you are therefore stuck with the built-in programs; it is not suitable for calculations outside the designed selection.

A calculator which falls halfway between the dedicated type and the advanced programmable, and is much cheaper than either, is the TI 58, which can be fitted with the same memory module of built-in programs as the TI 59 to do the basic navigation functions, and which is programmable. Its problem is that it has neither permanent memory nor a card reader, so programs need to be punched in every time it is switched on.

With the continuing development of hand-held calculators it must be appreciated that any list soon becomes out of date, and therefore the whole market should be looked at before deciding what to buy. For example, Casio have recently entered the field of possibilities with a programmable cassette tape reading calculator which has Alpha prompt as one of its features and this may prove to be as good as the HP and TI machines.

Chapter 7 **Radio Aids**

There are very few people navigating now who would dispute the importance of radio in various forms as an aid to navigation. The sophistication, ease of operation and reliability that have become available since the advent of the transistor and silicon chip has put radio fixing in one form or another within the reach of nearly everyone. Here I am using the term 'radio fixing' very loosely as I include all aids associated with radio under this broad heading (satellite navigators, Loran, Decca, etc). The days are long gone when a radio direction finding set was little more than a toy with which to waste time attempting to get hopelessly inaccurate bearings. The equipment now on the market is good enough to take all the guesswork out of position fixing, leaving the racing navigator free to spend more time on strategy, meteorology and other useful things.

Which Aids are Allowed?

Because the rule-makers will always lag behind new technological developments there will usually be a situation where there is equipment available for use that is banned in racing. Furthermore, different clubs have different rules and therefore the aids which are allowed will differ depending on where where you are sailing. In Britain, most offshore racing is done under the umbrella of the Royal Ocean Racing Club and so it is their rules which are most important to us. The RORC have decided, rightly or wrongly, on a fairly conservative policy on this subject, and the radio aids which they allow at present (1982) are very limited. To quote from their rules:

'Rule 12. Permitted Radio and Electronic Aids . . . (d) radio receiver, (e) radio direction finder to obtain bearing indication either by an aural minimum method, or by a meter provided to monitor the carrier level, or both. . . . No other electronic aid may be used.'

This part of Rule 12 very specifically defines the types of radio aid that is allowed. To put it into perspective, let us look at what it actually allows. 'An ordinary radio receiver' means that any radio position fixing system which can be picked up and used by means of an ordinary domestic radio receiver is allowed. Therefore Consol is allowed, and so are the new VHF 'radio lighthouses'. Part (e) of the Rule further allows radio direction finding sets that work on the principle of *manually* tuning an aerial to find the null and thus obtain a bearing. It does not allow for any kind of automatic or self-seeking direction finding sets, and in fact these are specifically prohibited later in the Rules.

ALL other types of radio aid are at present prohibited under RORC rules. However, my hope is that before too long that sentence could be deleted, as I feel very strongly that position fixing aids can only make the sport as a whole safer. Some countries allow other aids to be used; for example, Loran is permitted in the USA. And in a few races, any-thing goes – the Whitbread Round the World Race Committee have decided to allow *any* navigation aids and weather facsimile receivers.

Choice of Equipment for RORC Racing

Having said that the types of equipment allowed under the RORC rules is very limited, the range of available radio direction finders is still extremely varied. There are two basic choices that you have to make to start with. First, hand-held aerial (ferrite rod) or built-in masthead aerial (Beme loop). Except on steel or ferrocement yachts (which are seldom used for racing) I would always opt for a hand-held aerial system with a compass attached to the aerial. The problems with the fixed aerial system are twofold: the weight of the aerial is likely to be prohibitive, except on large yachts; and the bearings obtained will normally be relative to the ship's head and thus the course being steered at the moment the bearing is taken will need to be known, which introduces another source of potential error. With a hand-held aerial, on the other hand, the magnetic bearing of the beacon can be taken directly without needing to know the yacht's heading any more than roughly (for calculating deviation or quadrantal error if either of these has been calibrated for).

The second choice is between a built-in radio with separate DF aerial and a totally portable, self-contained radio and aerial. There are pros and cons to both types. The advantages of the portables are that they can be used anywhere on the yacht where the errors have been found to be at a minimum, and that the navigator can have his own set which he takes from one boat to another, thus ensuring familiarity.

Built-in radios with DF capability also have several advantages. Most important, perhaps, you often get facilities in the way of filters, frequency bands and methods of 'reading' the null which would be impracticable in a hand-held set. This can mean that decent bearings are obtained when the more limited type of set would have too much interference to give a good null. Built-in radios with their own loud-speakers are also easier to use for taking weather forecasts, etc than portable sets with only headphones. With most makes, the DF aerial lead can be long enough to enable a relatively error-free position to be used for taking the bearings.

Whether you are going for a portable or a built-in set, there are a few good and bad features to look for in choosing a RDF. As I have already said, the most important single feature for me is that the bearings obtained must (except on very large yachts) be magnetic bearings and *not* relative. In practice, therefore, the aerial part of the set must have a compass attached to it. The next item in my list of features to look for – the technical excellence of the receiver being assumed – is the ease of tuning the radio to the required frequency. The marine radiobeacon bandwidth is very narrow, so on an 'ordinary' radio it can be very difficult to separate one station from another. A RDF set must therefore have either an exceptionally large tuning dial together with a band-width selector switch especially for the marine beacons (such as the Sailor 108 or the B & G Homer) or a digital readout of frequencies (as in sets such as Lokata, B & G Homer 5, *et al.*). To have digital input of the desired frequency is perhaps not essential, although it can speed up station selection even more. I feel that sets which don't have either of these easy-tuning facilities should be relegated to the status of 'emergency use only'. Third, the exact position of the null must be obtainable even with a fairly weak signal or when there is a lot of interference from static or other stations. In reality this means that there must be at least two ways of identifying the null, audibly (preferably with headphones) and also with either a meter or a light which dims at the null. Whichever method is used, it is vital that it can be seen/heard from wherever the aerial is to be held.

Some sets offer facilities other than those listed above and they can be taken as bonuses (e.g. quartz clocks, built-in alarms, etc), but these should not over-ride the need for the features that are essential; others such as automatic DF contravene equipment rules.

This appears to be one of the few areas where you really do get what you pay for, and there seem to be three distinct price brackets. (1) The really cheap sets that are basic in function and not necessarily easy to use or robust, and which can really only be considered as back-up sets. (2) The top-range sets (Homer 5, Sailor, *et al.*) which have most or all of the functions you could wish for, and are constructed to almost military specifications. (3) The mid-range sets (Lokata, Aptel DDF 300, *et al.*) which have the same features as the top-range sets but are constructed using cheaper materials. There is a tendency towards the use of plastics rather than metal, particularly for the casings, and as a general rule they are not so well sealed against the water.

If I was footing the bill for an RDF, I would go for one of the mid-range sets, on the basis that it would give almost as good a result as the top-priced equipment and also that the very expensive models are likely to become outdated before they wear out (although the changes in newer equipment may not all be desired ones). If, on the other hand, I had no budget restrictions at all (someone else is paying?) then I would certainly rather have a set such as the Homer 5 as they are marginally nicer to use than most cheaper sets and the luxuries like the automatic alarm and the ability to key in frequencies for later use do make it a bit easier to get decent results.

Using Radio Direction Finders

Marine radiobeacons Most RDF position fixing around the British Isles at present uses the non-directional marine beacons which are placed along the coasts. To use the system to advantage requires knowing where to look up the relevant beacon information and how to interpret it. The information required can be found in several different publications: most nautical almanacs, Radio Signals Lists, NP 280 *Radio Services for Small Craft* and so on. Regardless of which source is used, the data required is the same and should include the following.

THE POSITION OF THE RADIOBEACON This is important since the beacon wanted may not be marked on the chart you happen to be using at the time. Also, it is quite common for the exact position of beacons to be moved from time to time as different aerials are brought into use and therefore the latest possible information should always be used.

THE CALL SIGN For marine beacons this will normally comprise two letters in Morse code. If you can't 'read' Morse then it is worthwhile learning at least the letters used by *your* most commonly utilised becons.

Some marine radiobeacons (such as Chichester Bar) also transmit a certain amount of coded information about the weather during their minute.

GROUPING Since the bandwidth available for marine radiobeacons is very limited, it is often necessary to group certain ones together on the same frequency and for them to transmit in rotation on a time-sharing basis. To make identification easier, each group has an individual tone. Not all beacons are grouped, however, and especially in North America many transmit continuously.

The system of grouping which is now almost universal around Europe is based on 1-minute transmissions within a cycle of 6 minutes; the complete group cycle always starts at the hour and is repeated every 6 minutes after that. Each beacon within a group is given a sequence number (or several if there are less than six in the group) and the table below shows the relationship between sequence number and transmission times.

Number in sequence	1	2	3	4	5	6
Transmits at	00	01	02	03	04	05
these minutes	06	07	08	09	10	11
past each hour	12	13	14	15	16	17
	18	19	20	21	22	23
	24	25	26	27	28	29
	30	31	32	33	34	35
	36	37	38	39	40	41
	42	43	44	45	46	47
	48	49	50	51	52	53
	54	55	56	57	58	59

LISTED RANGE OF THE BEACON This indicates the maximum useful range of the ground signal in nautical miles. At night it may be necessary to reduce the power of the transmissions in order to avoid causing interference with adjacent stations, in which case a second, smaller range will be given. As a general rule it is not safe to rely on MF (medium frequency) beacons around dawn and dusk, or at ranges in excess of about 70 nautical miles at night, because of the marked skywave effect.

MODES OF EMISSION Each radio beacon has its method of identification with regard to carrier waves and audio signals expressed as a symbol, as follows: A1   A2   A2*   A0A2. From the user's point of view this is only important so far as the switching on and off of the BFO (beat frequency oscillator) is concerned. (This facility is found on most receivers and produces an audio tone from an unmodulated carrier frequency: the BFO must be turned on in order to hear unmodulated signals, and off to hear modulated transmissions.) When to switch the BFO on/off for each mode of emission is shown in the following table.

Mode of emission	BFO switch during identification	BFO switch during DF signal period
A1	On	On
A2 and A2*	Off	Off
A0 A2	Off	On

Aerobeacons As their name indicates, aerobeacons are there for the convenience of aircraft and not primarily for yachts: their positions sometimes render them unsuitable for marine use due to land effects. Nautical almanacs, etc only tend to list those aerobeacons which are fairly suitable for use at sea. Quite often they can only be used reliably in specific sectors due to the intervention of high land between the beacon and the sea, so they should be used with caution especially if they are a long way inland. They are normally listed in a similar way to marine radiobeacons, with a few minor differences. Aerobeacons are normally identified by a three-letter call sign (compared to the usual two letters for marine beacons) and the Morse code for this is often transmitted at somewhat higher speed than for marine beacons. Aerobeacons do have the big advantage that they transmit continuously rather than in groups and so bearings can be obtained from them without having to wait for the appropriate place in a 6-minute cycle. Nearly all use AoA2 emission (thus requiring the BFO to be on during the DF period) whereas nearly all marine radiobeacons use either A2 or A2* modes, neither of which require the BFO to be switched on.

The signals transmitted by aerobeacons are fairly straightforward, consisting of: a continuous tone for DF purposes (BFO switched on) and the identification signal repeated at intervals of a few seconds (BFO switched off). Marine radiobeacons, on the other hand, normally transmit as follows. A 1-minute signal starting with the identification signal, repeated four times, followed by a continuous tone for about 25 seconds during which the bearing should be obtained. The beacon then 'signs off' by repeating its identification signal twice more. There is then a break of about 2 seconds before the next beacon in the group comes on the air.

Pre-planning radio fixes As well as extracting radiobeacon data from various publications for your floppy files and also putting the bulk of it onto the relevant charts, I put a table such as the one above on the bulkhead by the radio to remind me whether the BFO is needed or not for a particular beacon. In addition, it can often be worth planning each RDF fix. Knowing approximately where you are, it is possible to select the beacons which should, at least in theory, give the best fix, taking into account their range, the angle or 'cut' of the bearings, and so on. With an accurate timepiece it is then possible to decide on the order of getting the bearings, taking into account the beacons' positions in their respective sequences. This is made very easy with a set like the B & G Homer 5, where all the frequencies that are likely to be wanted can be keyed in before a race, to be recalled at the push of a single button. Pre-planning of a fix won't always work, as one or more of your selected beacons may not actually give a good signal for any number of reasons. It does, however, cut down by a considerable margin the time that most fixes take.

Taking bearings The position in the yacht that gives least error should have been determined at the start of the season. The required frequency is then selected and the beacon identified positively (normally with the BFO switched off). It is not good enough to assume that time and frequency on their own give a positive identification. (I once picked up a group operating on the same frequency as the one I wanted: they were a thousand miles away, but they still blanketed out the beacons I was anticipating.) Having identified the beacon, switch the BFO on if the mode of emission is AoA2 and tune the aerial for maximum signal. Next, swing the aerial to find the approximate position of the null and adjust the volume to suit the signal strength. Finally, go from side to side of the null as carefully as possible, adjusting the volume as necessary to get the smallest obtainable angle of null and read the compass at either side of the null. The mean of these readings should be the actual null, and the magnitude of their difference will give an indication of the likely accuracy of the bearing. If *no null* point can be obtained *do not rely* on the bearing, however strong the signal appeared.

With nearly all the sets I have used, I have found it easiest to get good bearings by holding the aerial at waist level, looking down on the compass and just rotating the aerial, not my body as well.

Likely errors when using non-directional radiobeacons

There are several sources of error which are likely to effect RDF bearings from non-directional beacons, some of which it is possible to calibrate for and some of which can only be deduced but not allowed for with corrections. The biggest single source of error is undoubtedly lack of experience. It can be rectified fairly easily, just by taking more bearings, especially when your position is known by other means. The more you do this the more accurate you will become, and more important, the more you will become aware of the level of accuracy that you can expect. The following paragraphs discuss the more important non-human errors.

Deviation A compass used to obtain RDF bearings is of course subject to deviation just as any other compass on a yacht. However, because it will often be a portable, hand bearing type of compass, this is one source of error that is all too easily disregarded or overlooked. (There is a common belief that hand bearing compasses are not influenced by deviation.) With this type of set, the bearings would ideally always be obtained with the aerial (and therefore the compass) in the same place in the yacht's magnetic environment. It is thus possible to determine the sort of deviation which is likely and even to make up a rough deviation card. It should be remembered, though, that a slight alteration in the position of the compass can affect the deviation considerably. Therefore when a suitable-seeming position has been found, it is worth checking the deviation all around it to ascertain the degree of error likely.

Re-radiation of radio signals Any part of the metal rigging or lifelines can, under the right circumstances, act as a radio aerial, re-radiating signals so that the bearing of that part of the rigging is obtained rather than the bearing of the radiobeacon. This effect can be minimized by reducing the number of 'closed loops' in the rigging, for example by insulating toggles at the ends of wires, using insulators or lashings at the ends of lifelines, etc. If all the rigging is fixed, then the residual error can be calibrated in the same sort of way as for deviation: you end up with a quadrantal error curve for the aerial which will be relative to the angle of the radio bearing from the yacht, and a deviation curve for the compass which is related to the yacht's heading. The accuracy of both of these error curves will depend on the RDF aerial and compass being used in the same place each time. Both curves need to be consulted and allowed for before a bearing is plotted. If you are very lucky, one or both of these will be negligible, which makes the plotting much easier. If your yacht has runners or other movable wire rigging, then it will be very difficult to get a meaningful error curve, and in any case the errors are likely to alter if the yacht is heeled.

Atmospheric effects Radio waves can be reflected and refracted by ionised air and this can cause quite severe errors in some circumstances. At dawn and dusk the ionisphere effect is particularly powerful and will therefore reflect radio waves back down to the earth more than at other times, which can mean that the sky wave is a stronger signal than the more directionally accurate ground wave (normally still all right at distances less than about 20 miles). Thunderstorms can also affect radio waves, by both causing interference and refracting the waves around large ionised clouds.

Coast refraction (land effect) Errors of as much as 5° can occur when a line of bearing from a radiobeacon cuts along a coast, more or less parallel or at a narrow angle to it, or where high ground lies between the beacon and the yacht. Land effect is very unpredictable, but once the radio wave has been refracted (bent) it will not then revert to its old course after the land has passed; even fairly small hills close to the beacon can cause quite large errors. This is largely what makes aerobeacons generally less reliable at sea level than purpose-designed marine beacons, since the former are often quite a long way inland.

It is therefore very important when selecting radiobeacons for a fix to try to choose those which have no high land intervening and which cross the coastline at large angles (greater than about 15°) in order to minimise the errors caused by land effect.

Radio Lighthouses

A type of directional VHF radiobeacon, commonly called a radio lighthouse in the marine context, has been under development and is presently (1982) operating on an experimental basis from four UK stations and one at Calais. The system is still in the trial stage and beacons may be added, discontinued or altered in their sectors or transmission characteristics as experience dictates. They are included in the usual Radio Signals Lists, and changes are in *Notices to Mariners.*

These radio lighthouses operate on VHF Channel 88 and have a range of about 20 miles, which is less than the usual range of MF beacons. They work on a completely different principle in that the directional information is in the transmission itself, and one obtains a bearing of the beacon within a 120° usable sector by simple counting with no need for a compass, directional aerial or special DF receiver. This is achieved in the same way that Consol works but because of the shorter ranges involved is much more accurate. An accuracy of 2° is claimed and in my experience this is actually maintained, almost regardless of the conditions and with need for very little practice. The system also has the potential to provide improved bearing information and additional facilities in the future, by modification of the beats in ways that can be detected by electronic listening devices but will not affect the audible signal.

After a Morse identifier and a 2-second long dash, the beacon transmits 67 beats, each corresponding to a 2° arc; the rate is two beats per second, to allow easy counting or timing with a stopwatch. The first four beats heard are disregarded, and then the number of beats until the silent null is counted (or derived from the stopwatch time). Knowing the bearings of the 120° usable sector of any beacon, because every beat heard after the fifth one represents 2° it is an easy matter to calculate your bearing from the beacon. For example, if the North Foreland sector is 240°–360°, beat 5 is 240°, beat 6 is 242°, etc: if 11 beats are heard before the null then 22° is added to the sector boundary of 240° giving your bearing as 252° True. Use is made even simpler by a table of bearings for the beacons, published in ALRS, or the Linton Navigation Protractor can be used to plot directly on the chart.

Although VHF directional beacons or radio lighthouses are not specifically allowed under present RORC rules, the Secretary has assured me that there is no intention to ban this form of fixing.

Consol

This long-range European aid to navigation is meant chiefly for aircraft but can be useful for yachts and ships as well. The Consol beacons (Ploneis in France and Stavanger in Norway) transmit a radiating pattern of dots and dashes, the total number of which add up to 60. By merely counting the number of dots and dashes heard, the great circle bearing of the beacon can be obtained (using tables in the *Admiralty List of Radio Signals* Vol. 5) or a Consol lattice chart can be easily read to get a line or area of position.

Although this is fine in theory, in practice Consol has limited use as it is not very accurate, at times giving errors of up to 10 or 12 miles at night. On long passage races such as the Fastnet, or transatlantic races, it can be a useful aid to confirm or check your DR position if celestial navigation is impossible or doubtful. Also, depending on your position, the Consol lattice may cover a biggish area for a given pair of counts. Most almanacs give further details on its use as do ALRS Vol. 5 or the pamphlet CAP 59. This is another form of radio fixing which *is* allowed by the RORC, and has the virtues of requiring only a simple long wave (LW) receiver and of longer range than radio beacons.

Currently Banned Radio Navaids

As the number of radio aids which are at present banned under RORC rules is likely to change as the cost of equipment comes down, this section looks very briefly at some of the available position-finding aids.

Sat-nav Satellite navigation systems used to be restricted to super-tankers and warships, but in recent years their cost has come down to little more than that of a good RDF set. The current generation of sat-nav sets work on the Doppler principle as the satellites move over-head, and the system is based on a number of satellites in polar orbit. In order to get a good fix there must be a satellite within 'view' and at a reasonable angle above the horizon. This will happen on average every half to three-quarters of an hour, though bunching does occur and gives longer gaps, and so it is possible that the set will need to have been switched on for some time before a fix is obtained. It is therefore normal to leave the set on permanently while at sea to cut down warm-up time. Most available models have some kind of automatic dead reckoning facility to update the yacht's position between good fixes, and the accuracy of a good fix is remarkable being measured in yards rather than miles. It is interesting that the 1981–2 Whitbread Round the World Race allowed sat-nav for safety in high latitudes.

Loran C Loran was developed in the USA and is allowed there for most racing. One of the special receivers will give a fix to within about a quarter of a mile. Automatic Loran sets translate the signals received to give a lat.–long. position with no further work necessary, and can give course corrections to requested destinations or waypoints. At present the cover of ground wave transmissions does not extend into the English Channel but it does cover Ireland, North Wales and Scotland, Scandinavia and the East Coast as far down as East Anglia. Thus transatlantic navigators can use it except when closing or leaving the British Isles. Mediterranean coverage is good. The sky wave cover, which is still usable although less accurate than the ground wave (especially at night), extends over almost the whole of the navigable portion of the Northern Hemisphere. It is possible that another Loran C transmitter will eventually be installed in North France to extend the ground wave cover, but this may be unlikely due to the more sophisticated systems available for the future.

Omega Primarily a long range fixing system, which will provide a position to within a mile anywhere on earth. It operates from nine stations set up in various countries which generate phase-stable signals on 10.2 kHz, controlled by atomic clocks. The receiver tracks all the stations at once and gives a readout of three position lines after certain predictable errors are fed in for the machine to make corrections with. Omega is at present still in the process of development and should therefore be used with caution. This is particularly true in high latitudes where the accuracy may be affected by polar ice cap absorption. However, the cost of Omega sets puts it out of reach for most yacht owners, for whom Loran C or sat-nav are now better and cheaper alternatives.

Decca Navigator A medium range navigational system with extreme accuracy, which is widely used in surveying and by fishing boats and coasters. It has quite a high power drain, though, and once set up must be left on more or less permanently which makes it not very suitable for use on racing yachts. The equipment necessary to receive the signals has been available only on a rental basis; it processes the signals into a form which can be plotted on charts overprinted with Decca lattices. However, a new development is Decca equipment which utilises the transmissions to give a lat.-long. position directly, although without quite the same accuracy since known local distortions of the lattice are not allowed for. Decca Navigator sets of this type and designed for yachts have recently become available for purchase.

Chapter 8 **True and Apparent Wind**

Calculating the wind velocity and direction to a reasonable degree of accuracy are a necessary part of most racing navigation. In order to do any such calculations it is obviously essential to have wind speed and direction instruments: therefore all the calculations in this chapter will only be of real use to navigators on yachts so equipped, although the basic principles involved will be useful to anyone.

All wind instruments presently available indicate the apparent wind speed and direction at the instrument head, so we need to look at how this information can be used directly and also how the readings can be modified to obtain true wind information. To start with, let us look at the differences between true and apparent wind. If a yacht is stationary (relative to the ground), upright and has no sails hoisted, then obviously the apparent wind acting on her is the same as the true wind. However, if any of these factors do not apply the instruments will not give true wind readings. So, if the yacht is moving forwards, making leeway, drifting with the stream, pitching, heeling or any combination of these, the true wind will be modified and become apparent wind.

Vectors Affecting Apparent Wind

The next thing to examine is exactly how all these factors change the wind direction and velocity.

Boat speed As a yacht moves forward through the water a headwind is generated, and this headwind will be equal in speed to that of the yacht but opposite in direction (Fig. 8.1). If there is any wind other than that generated by the yacht's movement, then fairly obviously the wind direction will be moved forwards (come more from ahead); and apparent wind velocity will be increased if the true wind is from forward of the beam (Fig. 8.2) and decreased if it is aft of the beam.

8.1 A boat's forward movement generates a headwind Ws that is equal to her speed forward Vs and in the opposite direction.

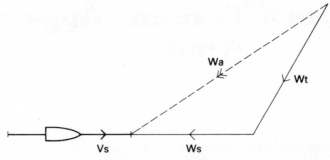

8.2 The headwind Ws generated by a boat's movement modifies any true wind that is blowing. This resultant, the apparent wind Wa, comes more from ahead and increases.

Leeway Just as forward motion modifies the true wind, so must sideways motion. Leeway is defined as movement to leeward in a direction at right angles to the fore-and-aft line of the yacht; in modern yachts it is only likely to be significant when the wind is forward of the beam, and in waves. This means that leeway will always reduce the apparent wind velocity and make the apparent wind come more from ahead (Fig. 8.3), and therefore leeway is not only detrimental in the obvious sense of taking you to leeward of your destination but also actually 'heads' you and slows the boat down as there is less wind.

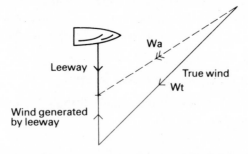

8.3 The apparent wind draws ahead and decreases as a result of leeway.

Angle of heel The usual cup type of anemometer is only accurate when the shaft is at right angles to the wind flow, and will give high readings when the yacht is heeled. Wind vanes are also affected by angle of heel, the amount of error being dependent on apparent wind direction as well as the angle of heel.

Pitching As a yacht pitches fore and aft in waves the apparent wind flowing over both the wind instruments and the sail is modified. The wind will appear to strengthen and head you as the mast pitches forward, and to go lighter and free as it swings back. This can give rise to wildly fluctuating instrument readings unless the instruments are quite heavily damped (or averaged) and care is therefore required in the interpretation of the readings before they can be used. Another aspect of the variation in wind flow is that the changing angles of attack of the apparent wind on the sails will necessitate different sheeting positions and tensions than in calmer water, since more twist will be required so that at least part of the sails are set correctly at any one moment. Going upwind, this can often mean different settings for the sheet on each tack due to the differing angles of the waves.

Current-induced wind Whenever a vessel is not attached to the sea-bed she will be drifting with the current or stream whether it is permanent (rivers, ocean currents) or temporary (tidal) in nature, and therefore the apparent wind will be modified by this drift. For most purposes, however, this can be ignored as the amount of modification to the wind will remain the same irrespective of her speed or heading. The only times that currents need to be taken into account in apparent wind calculations are when the direction or velocity of the current is going to change, e.g. when sailing from inshore out into the main stream, or at the change in the tide. In practical terms this means that if we are already in the current then its effect is already being felt and so far as the yacht is concerned the 'true wind' is the actual wind plus the current vector. This is normally referred to as the 'modified wind' to differentiate it from the true (unmodified by current) and apparent (changed by boat's own motion) wind. If, however, the current is going to change for any reason then it is important to understand how different directions/velocities of current combine with the movement of the yacht to change her apparent wind. The following paragraphs look at these changes in detail.

Modification of apparent wind by current – upwind sailing It is probably more important for the navigator to understand the changes in apparent wind due to current (stream) when going upwind than on any other point of sailing. Fig. 8.4 is a basic diagram to illustrate how the true wind (Wt) is modified by boat speed (Vs) to give apparent wind (Wa); Ws is the wind induced by the boat's forward motion and has same velocity but opposite direction to Vs. Figs 8.5 to 8.8 add the vector of current-induced wind to the basic diagram to show whether the apparent wind has headed or lifted, increased or decreased, in each case.

Fig. 8.9 shows that whenever the current is to windward of the un-modified apparent wind direction, then the yacht is headed; and

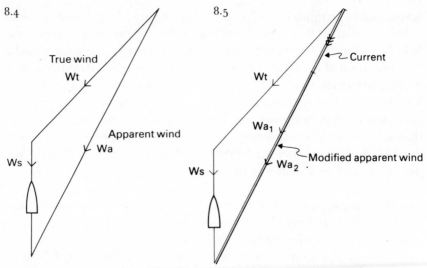

8.4 The basic vector diagram showing apparent wind as a resultant of the true wind and the headwind generated by the boat's speed.

8.5 Effect on apparent wind when current is going in the same direction. The modified apparent wind Wa_2 is still in the same direction but its velocity is reduced: this is shown by the vector for Wa_2 being in the same direction but shorter than that representing the unmodified apparent wind Wa_1.

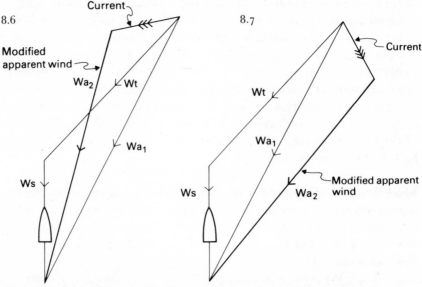

8.6 Apparent wind Wa_1 modified by a current coming at a large angle on the windward side. The current modified wind Wa_2 is heading the boat and in this case is less strong; if the current were to come from more on the beam or aft of the beam, the Wa_2 vector would lengthen (see Figs 8.9–10).

8.7 When the current is on the leeward side the apparent wind lifts, and at this angle its velocity is decreased. As in Fig. 8.6, as the current swings to come from farther off the bow the length (speed) of vector Wa_2 increases.

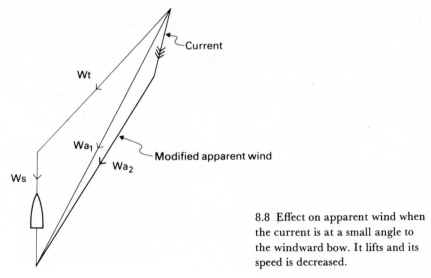

Current

Wt

Wa₁

Wa₂ — Modified apparent wind

Ws

8.8 Effect on apparent wind when the current is at a small angle to the windward bow. It lifts and its speed is decreased.

conversely, if the current is to leeward of the apparent wind then the yacht is freed. Fig. 8.10 illustrates the same sort of thing but with regard to velocity rather than direction. It can be seen that if the current is coming from forward of a line perpendicular to the apparent wind direction, then the apparent wind velocity is reduced, and vice versa. (These diagrams relate to and explain the much abused term 'lee-bow effect' further discussed in Chapter 9.)

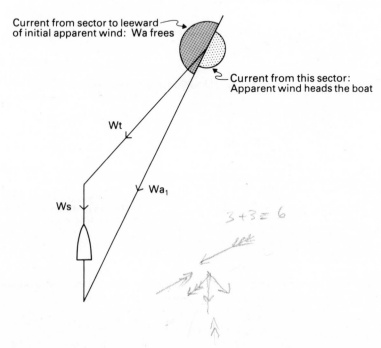

Current from sector to leeward of initial apparent wind: Wa frees

Current from this sector: Apparent wind heads the boat

Wt

Wa₁

Ws

8.9

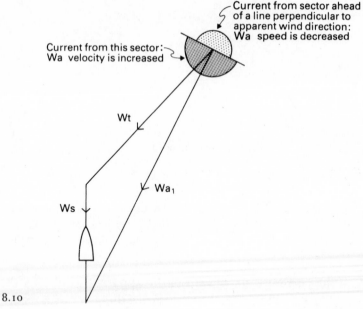

Current from sector ahead
of a line perpendicular to
apparent wind direction:
Wa speed is decreased

Current from this sector:
Wa velocity is increased

Wt

Wa₁

Ws

8.10

The main use of this information is in determining what the yacht's heading will be on either tack when the current has changed direction or rate. The easiest way to calculate the new headings on each tack is probably to add the current or tide-induced wind vector to the true wind vector to give a modified true wind, as shown in Fig. 8.11. The courses steered through the water on each tack can then easily be obtained just through knowing the tacking angle of the yacht in that wind strength.

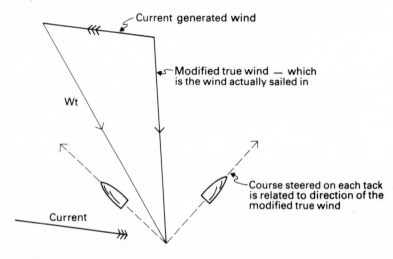

Current generated wind

Modified true wind — which
is the wind actually sailed in

Wt

Course steered on each tack
is related to direction of the
modified true wind

Current

8.11 Effect of current on true wind direction, i.e. the wind that the yacht would 'feel' if drifting on the current with no boat speed from the sails.

Tacking to Lay a Mark in a Tideway

One problem that the navigator encounters quite frequently is in determining just where the layline is for a windward mark in a cross-tide or cross-current, as illustrated in Fig. 8.12. Clearly, in such a case one has to make allowance for the tide and Fig. 8.13 shows that the solution to the problem is in effect the reverse of setting a course. The stream direction and rate is set off on the chart *towards* the mark. Then, assuming that the yacht's heading and probable speed on the new tack are known, this vector can be laid off from the end of the stream vector: the end of this second vector is then joined up with the weather mark to give the layline. If the yacht is not sailing in the same stream that she will be in while sailing towards the mark (as in the case of going inshore to cheat the tide and having to stand out again to a mark in the full stream), then the modified true wind will have to be calculated first, as shown in the previous section.

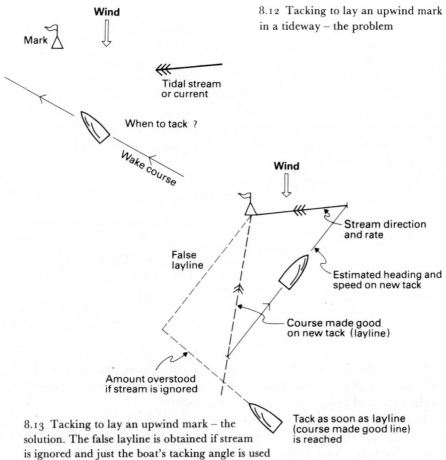

8.12 Tacking to lay an upwind mark in a tideway – the problem

8.13 Tacking to lay an upwind mark – the solution. The false layline is obtained if stream is ignored and just the boat's tacking angle is used

Calculating the New Apparent Wind

One of the navigator's many tasks is to inform the crew what the apparent wind direction and velocity are going to be on the next leg and in enough time to get the appropriate sails ready. This is another calculation that can only be worked out with any degree of accuracy by using wind instruments.

It is probably easiest to consider the calculation in three stages. First, the course to the next mark is obviously known as this is what is being steered at present; the apparent wind for the present leg can be read off the instruments and therefore the true wind can be calculated. This will in fact be the true wind modified by the current (if any), but unless the current is going to be different on the next leg this does not matter. Fig. 8.14 reminds you of the basic vector diagram used to solve this part of the problem.

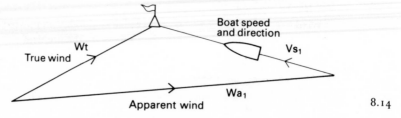

8.14

The second stage of the problem is to calculate the course to steer on the next leg by doing a straightforward 'shaping' vector diagram as in Fig. 8.15.

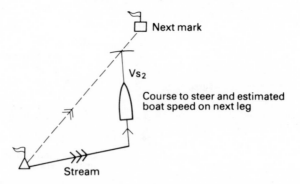

8.15

Finally, the true wind and course steered vectors obtained in the previous two steps have to be combined to give the direction and speed of the expected apparent wind as in Fig. 8.16.

In practice these three diagrams can be combined into one in order to simplify the drawing. This complete diagram can be constructed in one of two ways. The method I prefer to use is shown in Fig. 8.17, with

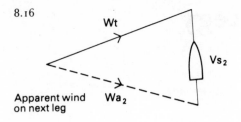

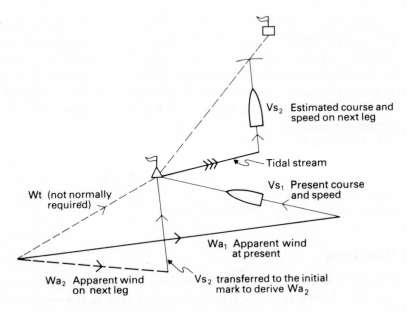

8.17 Diagram to calculate new apparent wind

the new course to steer line Vs(2) being transferred rather than the true wind Wt line. This saves some drawing.

This apparent wind strength and heading information can be used in conjunction with a sail-change polar diagram (Chapter 5) so that the navigator can tell the crew which sails will be required and where they should be sheeted, at least as a starting point.

Chapter 9 **Strategy**

Strategy has been defined as 'the art of war' and I feel that this is a fairly apt definition for offshore racing. So far as this chapter is concerned, strategy is the 'art' of deciding where to go and how to get there in the absence of other protagonists. Although in an actual race the strategic decisions may well be influenced or even over-ridden by the dictates of tactics relating to other yachts, it is with strategy that the racing navigator normally concerns himself.

It is easiest to consider each part of the race separately in making strategic decisions, as the strategy of the previous leg becomes totally obsolete as the next turning mark is reached. The following therefore takes each leg of the course individually and looks at the strategy involved with examples where relevant.

Starting

The one time in the race when tactical considerations are almost bound to over-ride strategic desires is the start, but even so it is vital to have a clear plan of what the ideal start would be in any forseeable situation, assuming the other competitors let you carry out this plan. Obviously you should aim to arrive at the line sailing at full speed as the gun goes, and for this it is largely the judgement of the helmsman that is called into play with the navigator probably just doing the timing. However, the decision about which part of the line to start on is almost certainly the navigator's problem.

Tideless upwind starts Assuming that the start is basically upwind and the first leg is a beat from anywhere on the line, then in a situation where there is no stream deciding which end of the line is favoured is quite easy. In Fig. 9.1 it can be seen that if the line is absolutely square to the wind then there is no distance advantage to either end. However, as starboard tack boats have right of way over those on port tack, in this case starting on port tack would obviously be suicidal. Furthermore, if a yacht started at the 'port end' of the line on starboard tack, she would be unable to tack onto port until all the yachts to windward of her had done so as she would not be able to clear them after a tack. This means that if the line is unbiased as far as wind direction is concerned it is best to start at the starboard end if freedom to tack on wind shifts is wanted after the start. There are times when this is not the case, for example when there is much less foul tide on the port side of the course or if a wind bend is expected on that side, but as a general rule the starboard end of the line on starboard tack is the place to be if the line is square to the wind.

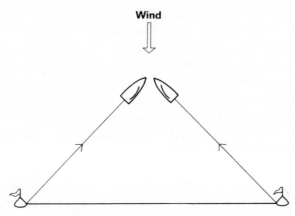

9.1 Square starting line at right angles to the wind direction and with no stream: neither end has any distance advantage.

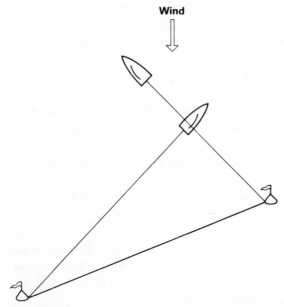

9.2 Effect of starboard end bias on the line. The yacht which started at that end crosses well in front, when boat speeds are similar.

If the line is biased as in Fig. 9.2 so that the starboard end is upwind, then it is obviously even more important to start at the starboard end as a yacht starting at the port end would actually be behind one that had started at the starboard end when they first crossed tacks. Because with a square or starboard biased line it is so important to be at the starboard end at the start, a lot of bunching is caused with premature starters and possibly general recalls, so a good race committee will often try to give a line some port end bias. This gives yachts starting at the port end of the line a distance advantage over those at the starboard end, but the starboard end starter still has the right-of-way advantage and is able to tack on wind shifts more easily.

With port end bias, the absolutely ideal place to start is at the port end of the line and on port tack to allow a quick flip onto starboard at the first wind shift, though this is obviously a pretty dangerous manoeuvre. If you arrive at the line on port tack at all late, then you're forced into ducking behind any on-time starboard tackers, which may be half the fleet; and even if the timing is exactly right any early starters on starboard tack can still mess up your start. This all means that the time to attempt a port end start is when there is a lot of port bias, there are likely to be frequent wind shifts, and the rest of the fleet is of mediocre standard at starting! At other times when a port end start is indicated, it is probably better to compromise little and start at the port end (to gain the distance advantage) but on starboard tack so as to retain the right of way. From the point of view of the race officer this makes for a better start as the fleet will tend to spread itself all the way along the line as each yacht attempts to compromise to best advantage.

Measuring the bias Having considered the theory of which end to start from, the next thing is working this out in practice. I favour first of all finding the exact compass bearing of the start line by sighting along it from beyond the end, to enable the distance marks to be used as transits, and then finding the true wind direction by shooting up head-to-wind and noting the compass heading. This should be done at least three or four times before the start to enable an accurate picture of the wind direction to be built up, and to make it easier it can be noted each time the yacht tacks in the pre-start manoeuvres. Ideally, the wind direction should be checked at each end of the line otherwise a wind bend along the line might go unnoticed. Having obtained both the wind direction and the bearing of the line, I find it safest to draw both on the chart to find which end, if either, is favoured, although obviously this can be calculated arithmetically.

Upwind starts with tidal stream The relatively simple situation that we have dealt with so far can become slightly more complicated if there is a current or tidal stream to take into account. This is particu-

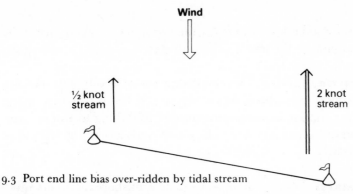

9.3 Port end line bias over-ridden by tidal stream

larly true if there is a difference in the stream from one end of the line to the other, as illustrated in Fig. 9.3. In such cases the bias on the line due to the wind direction still has to be taken into account, but it might be nullified, or enhanced, by the tidal stream. Where conditions vary along the line, it is therefore necessary to calculate the amount of advantage to be gained from the line bias and compare it with the possible disadvantage of the extra foul stream or less fair stream: again, some form of compromise will probably have to be made.

If the stream is constant over the whole starting area then it can be ignored when deciding on which end of the line to start, except in so far as it affects the direction/velocity of the apparent wind. As was shown in Chapter 8, the tidal stream will cause the true wind to be 'modified' and it is this modified wind direction which must be used for determining the bias on the line. This will nearly always be done automatically as the yacht will be drifting on the stream when she is put head-to-wind to find the wind direction; it will only need to be calculated as shown in Fig. 9.4 if she is at anchor or on a mooring when the true wind is being determined.

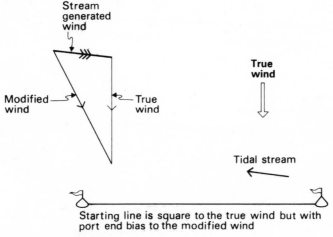

Starting line is square to the true wind but with port end bias to the modified wind

9.4 Effect of stream on bias of the starting line

If the tidal stream allows you to lay the first mark from one end of the line, this is obviously the end at which to start.

Upwind starting tactics The detailed tactics of how best to start are covered in almost every book on racing tactics, but it is worth saying here that clear wind after the start is the essential thing to aim for, and that as a general rule it is better to be ten seconds late at the start than two seconds early.

Fixed line starts For reasons of convenience, offshore races very often start from a fixed line rather than from a committee-boat line, and this of course means that the starts are very often not to windward. Although this is not normally so satisfactory as an upwind start from the point of view of the competitors, it is a fact of life and therefore the strategic consequences of downwind starts need to be looked at. Another point worth considering with fixed lines is that their position is known before the race and therefore a lot of pre-planning can be done, particularly with regard to tidal streams and likely wind bends or shifts around the starting area. (The pre-planning aspect of starting was discussed in Chapter 4.)

With a downwind start it is the bias of the line with regard to the direction of the first leg of the course which needs to be considered, rather than the bias in relation to the wind direction. However, although it is the bias of the line in relation to the first leg that will favour one end in terms of distance to the first mark, the wind direction obviously needs to be taken into account as well. On a reaching start the upwind end of the line will ensure clear wind and this may be of

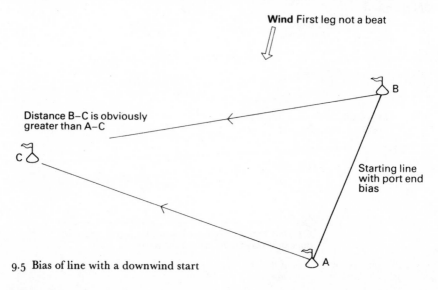

9.5 Bias of line with a downwind start

paramount importance, particularly in a small boat which would be driven over by larger ones with consequent loss of wind if she started to leeward. With larger boats the need for clear wind needs to be balanced against the possibility of a faster point of sailing to the first mark by starting at the leeward end of the line. Ideally the speed polar diagram would be studied to ascertain whether the slightly higher course would give a significant increase in speed, or if the leeward start would merely risk your being blanketed by the rest of the fleet. As with upwind port tack starts, the relative starting expertise of your helmsman compared to the rest of the fleet can provide another guide. If you can expect to get away better than most other yachts then a leeward start will very often pay, while if your starting is below average it is probably better to start with clear air for a long way to windward of you.

If the start is dead downwind, or nearly so, a different set of criteria come into play. Once again the distance to the first mark should be considered, and then the favoured gybe for the first part of the run. Assuming it is not windy enough to allow dead square running without significant loss of speed, one gybe is almost bound to be favoured and the position on the line at the start must allow one to reach up enough to maintain a fast speed without having to cross the whole fleet while doing so. If the first turning mark is quite close to the start, it might well be necessary to consider the requirements on reaching the mark before the start, and then possibly cross the line in a position to ensure that an inside berth at the mark is possible.

With a downwind start there is even more to be lost by being too early than with a beating start, and there is not quite the urgency of being at the line exactly at the gun either since even a late starter will probably have clear wind. So the message here is: obviously, be as close to the line as possible, but never overdo it and be over at the start.

Strategy Upwind

The beat is nearly always the leg of the course which requires most strategic decisions. The timing and position of each tack are very often critical, with major gains to be had by getting it right and large losses to be made if you tack at the wrong time. While the decision in any one case may be very complicated, involving many items of data, the individual units of this data are relatively simple. The following analysis will therefore start with basic situations involving single sets of parameters and then go on to more complicated problems.

Steady wind direction If the wind direction is truly steady, with no shifts, bends, veers or backs, there is no need for any strategy at all.

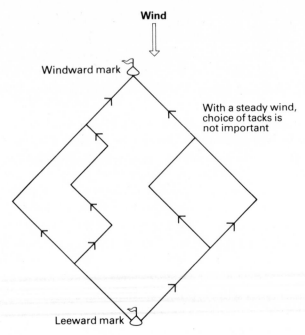

9.6 Beating in constant wind direction

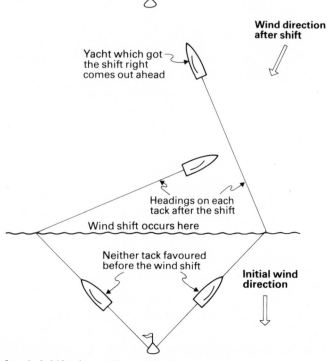

9.7 Effect of a wind shift when sailing upwind

When to tack will be dictated by tactical considerations relating to the other competitors more than by anything else. If there is a changing tidal stream then it will require strategic decisions, but this situation is dealt with later; here it is only wind which is being considered. This simplest of all beating situations is shown in Fig. 9.6.

Unexpected wind shifts In practice, the situation described above rarely if ever happens. Even if the wind is basically steady in direction there will nearly always be the occasional shift, and in the absence of tidal stream the shifts should be used to best advantage. Since the wind is probably likely to shift it is obviously dangerous to go too far to one side or the other of the rhumb line as otherwise one might end up on the wrong side of a shift thereby increasing the distance to the mark (Fig. 9.7). Many a race has been lost from a position of a long early lead by ignoring this principle.

If this potentially disastrous situation is to be avoided, some form of limiting lines need to be put down on either side of the beat. On a relatively long leg and in the absence of other complications, one way to do this is to tack down sectors, as shown in Fig. 9.8, which reduces any losses that might be sustained. It also stops any gains from a lucky shift being large and so while a yacht which takes a flyer *may* come out ahead of a more conservative boat, the difference should not be too great.

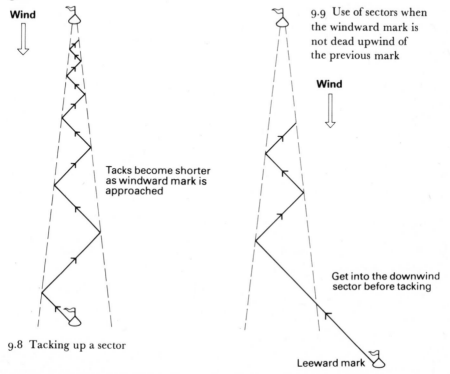

Wind

9.9 Use of sectors when the windward mark is not dead upwind of the previous mark

Wind

Tacks become shorter as windward mark is approached

Get into the downwind sector before tacking

9.8 Tacking up a sector

Leeward mark

The exact size of this sector is not critical but I have found that 10° is about right in most cases. When plotting the sector on the chart it is important to make sure that the sector is dead downwind from the mark, and if the wind does shift and stay shifted then the new 'downwind' sector should be used. This means that if the leeward mark is not dead downwind from the windward mark, the first tack away from the leeward mark should be made long enough to take the yacht to the far side of the chosen downwind sector. This sounds complicated but is explained by Fig. 9.9.

Appropriate sectors can be marked on the chart before the race, labelling each with the magnetic bearing of each side of the sector (Fig. 9.10).

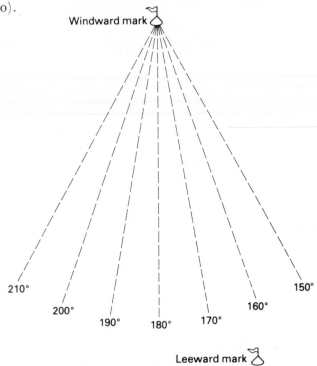

9.10 Sectors drawn on a chart before a race. The sector edges are marked with the wind direction (magnetic) with which they should be used.

Let us recap on how to use wind shifts. In the ideal situation one would always be on the gaining tack, i.e. the tack which is taking you towards the mark fastest, and so every shift should be looked at with this in mind. However, once you have reached a point exactly downwind from the mark the gaining tack will change as soon as you sail a few yards away from this point, hence the sectors to stop you going out on a limb too far away from the dead downwind line while not making each leg stupidly short.

Expected wind shifts If the wind is expected to shift one way or the other, then this can be used to try to get on the right side of the beat when the shift arrives. As can be seen from Fig. 9.11, if a veer is expected then you should go to the right of the beat in anticipation, and vice-versa if the wind is expected to back.

As wind prediction is a fairly imprecise science, the situation will normally be that while a shift is expected the exact timing and angular change will rarely be known. This means that while the side of the course that you should be on will be known, just how far to the right or left would be ideal will probably be in doubt, which further means that sectors are still useful as limiting lines even when a shift is expected. If, for example, the wind is forecast to veer then one might sail in the sector 10° to the right of the initial downwind sector, as shown in Fig. 9.11. As before, doing this cuts your losses if the expected shift does not materialise while still allowing a reasonable gain from it. If you are very sure of the timing and magnitude of the wind shift then it may be reasonable to sail up to 20° towards the expected new direction but it will rarely be sensible to go much beyond this as the dangers of either overstanding the mark if the shift is larger/earlier than expected, or being way out on a limb if the shift is late, start to increase dramatically.

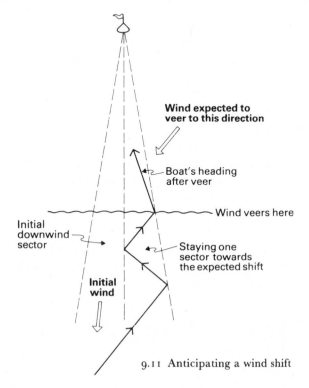

9.11 Anticipating a wind shift

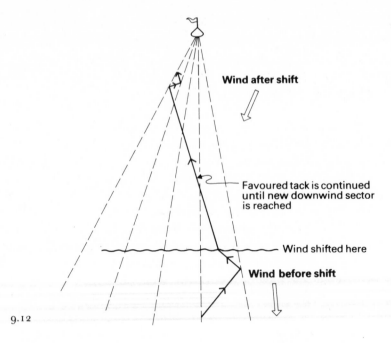

Wind after shift

Favoured tack is continued
until new downwind sector
is reached

Wind shifted here

Wind before shift

9.12

Once a wind shift occurs, whether or not it is expected you should go onto the now favoured tack and stay on it until the new downwind sector is reached. This is shown in Fig. 9.12 where it can be seen that all one is really doing is staying on the favoured tack for as long as reasonable in every case. Only if a further shift is expected should you remain in a more windward sector.

Wind bends By a wind bend I mean a change in wind direction which gets greater and greater as time goes on. This can be caused by many different things, such as the gradual veer as a depression passes by to the north or the bend which is experienced as a coastline is approached. In practice, the difference between a bend and a shift is that you should use the latter as soon as it occurs (in case the wind shifts back again) whereas if a boat gets onto the favoured tack as soon as a bend is encountered then she will sail straight out of the bend back into a 'header' in a lot of cases and will not make best use of the bend. The advantage which can be gained by sailing into the heading bend and thus taking an initial setback can be seen in Fig. 9.13.

Beating with a cross-tide So far we have only considered the strategy of sailing upwind in a tideless situation whereas in reality there will very often be a current or tidal stream to be taken into account as well as wind shifts.

If the direction and rate of stream are going to remain constant

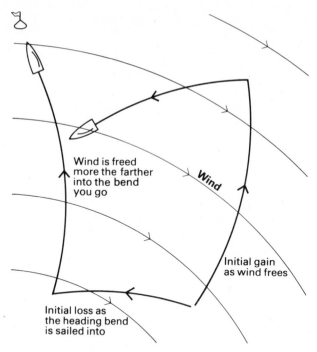

Wind is freed
more the farther
into the bend
you go

Wind

Initial gain
as wind frees

Initial loss as
the heading bend
is sailed into

9.13 Sailing into a wind bend for maximum advantage

throughout the beat then the situation is not much more complicated than with no stream. The principle of sailing in sectors can still be used, the only difference being that the sector used should be the one centred about the average course made good (allowing for current or tidal set) rather than about the average course steered as before. This works because it means that the same amount of time will be spent on each tack. Obviously the 'average course steered' has to take into account the modified wind direction if it is being worked out beforehand, but if the actual courses steered on each tack are used then this will automatically take it into account.

The real complications with tidal streams come when the tide is going to change during the course of the beat. As was shown in Chapter 8, if a cross-tide is going to change from one direction to another while beating and this change alters which tack is the lee-bowing one, then it will pay to be on the lee-bowing tack for as long as possible, which probably means tacking at the change of the tide. It is therefore important in a cross-tide situation that the principle of sailing in sectors is modified to take this into account. All that really happens when the tide turns is that the modified wind direction changes correspondingly, and in effect this is just a totally predictable wind shift and should be used as such. Fig. 9.15 shows the effect of two different tidal streams during a beat, in this case in opposite directions. The amount of

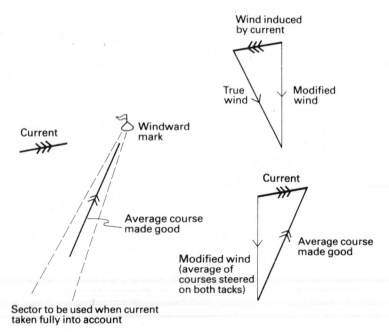

Wind induced
by current

True
wind

Modified
wind

Current

Windward
mark

Average course
made good

Current

Average course
made good

Modified wind
(average of
courses steered
on both tacks)

Sector to be used when current
taken fully into account

9.14 Use of limiting sectors with a cross-tide

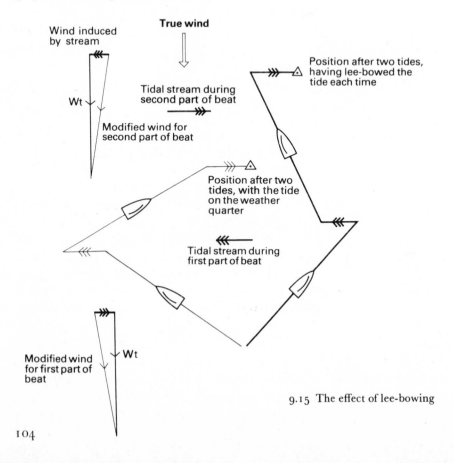

Wind induced
by stream

True wind

Wt

Tidal stream during
second part of beat

Modified wind for
second part of beat

Position after two tides,
having lee-bowed the
tide each time

Position after two
tides, with the tide
on the weather
quarter

Tidal stream during
first part of beat

Modified wind
for first part of
beat

Wt

9.15 The effect of lee-bowing

modification that there is to the wind direction will depend on the relative strengths of true wind and tidal stream and the example shown uses a ratio of 5:1 (e.g. 10 knots true wind and 2 knots stream), which is by no means extraordinary. The lighter the wind and/or the stronger the tide, the more it is important to get this right.

The aim should be to stay on the *favoured* tack (i.e. the one with the best Vmg towards the mark) for as long as possible and in a lot of cases this will mean lee-bowing the tide for as long as possible. In practice, assuming the lee-bow tack to be the favourable one, it should be held on to for the whole tide so long as the windward mark will not be over-stood on the other tack on the next tide. When the final change of tide before reaching the mark happens, the navigator should attempt to calculate where the layline will be once the tidal stream has reached its maximum strength and sail almost to this layline while the new tide is still relatively slack. This makes use of the principle of sailing into a wind bend, as already discussed. Obviously care must be exercised when doing this to ensure that the mark is not overstood (think a little bit on the conservative side), and once the tidal stream has reached its

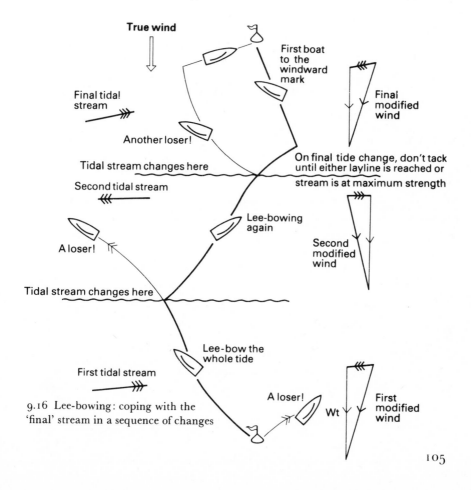

9.16 Lee-bowing: coping with the 'final' stream in a sequence of changes

maximum rate (i.e. the apparent wind has been shifted by the tide as much as it is going to be) one might as well go onto the lee-bow tack even if the layline has not been reached. This rather complicated sounding sequence is shown diagrammatically in Fig. 9.16.

If a wind shift is expected in addition to the one caused by the change in the stream, then it also has to be allowed for by going towards the expected shift before putting in the final tack just as one would do if there was no stream to worry about. In essence, what one is doing is attempting to combine all the wind shifts however caused into one formula so that their combined effect can be calculated.

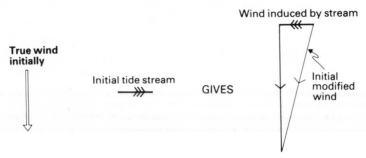

The wind is forecast to veer at about the time of the change of the tide:

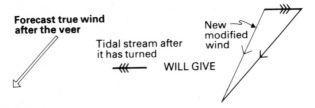

But, if the wind doesn't veer as expected:

9.17 An expected wind shift conflicting with a shift due to change of tide

In Fig. 9.17 there is an expected shift to the right (a veer), and the amount of faith that one puts in this forecast will dictate whether to lee-bow the first tide (in case the shift does not happen) or sail to the right of the rhumb line to be ready for the shift when it comes. In this particular example, if the shift occurs as forecast there will not be a great gain from it as compared to the initial lee-bow gain and it is probably best to sail a middle path in such a case. If the shift comes later than expected or is not so large as anticipated then less will be lost than if the initial lee-bow was ignored. If the shift comes as expected or earlier, then once again not too much will be lost.

This type of fairly conservative strategy is the sort that wins a series of races, giving consistently good results but perhaps without winning many individual races, that honour being left to the person who is prepared to risk all on a forecast wind. Sometimes the forecast is so positive that it is worth taking the extreme path, but not often.

If a shift is expected that will enhance the gains made by lee-bowing, such as in Fig. 9.18, then one should obviously stay on the lee-bowing tack and only consider the wind shift at the turn of the tide, when the situation becomes as it was in the previous example.

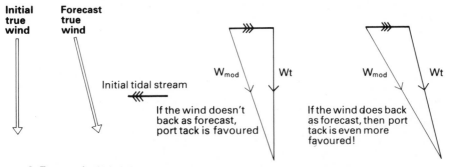

9.18 Expected wind shift enhancing the lee-bow effect when beating

Beating when the stream and wind are in the same direction

This is the situation that will usually be encountered when sailing along a coast rather than across a channel or an open stretch of water. In a lot of ways it is much simpler as the changes in tidal stream do not significantly alter the apparent wind direction, merely affecting the strength of the apparent wind and the yacht's speed over the ground. This means that in open waters where there is no coast nearby there is nothing strategic that one can do about the tidal stream and therefore wind shifts should be the deciding factors, not tide changes.

However, if a coastline is relatively handy then this may well allow some strategic decisions with regard to the tidal stream. If, for example, a bay with weak tides can be sailed into while the tide is foul then this would obviously be good, heading back out into the stronger stream when the tide is about to turn in one's favour. There are dangers to attempting to use the coastline in this way, though. Except in a sea breeze the wind is likely to be lighter close to the land and so the overall speed over the ground may not increase by the amount that one had hoped for. Indeed, in a bay skirted by high ground you may end up becalmed inshore while the fleet sails past out in stronger wind as well as tide! Another problem which may occur while trying to get out of the foul tide is a 'mistake' in the timing. Unless you can be reasonably sure of getting out of the tide at the right time, and also of not arriving at a headland with even stronger foul tide, then once again it may be more sensible to stay out in the relatively strong streams offshore. To get this tide-dodging right means correctly predicting the wind speeds and tidal stream rate inshore, and thereby boat speed over the ground; and also when the tide will turn, which is not necessarily as per published predictions.

One example of this was in the 1979 Fastnet when the fleet split in its endeavours to get round Portland Bill (a long point reaching out into the Channel) against a foul spring tide. Half the fleet went inshore only to stop dead at the Bill, where tides were reported to be in excess of 5 knots. The others went straight from St Alban's Head out on starboard tack while the tide was still favourable and thus passed at least 5 miles south of the Bill, missing the very strong inshore tide but being in the main stream of between 2 and 3 knots for a whole six hours. I opted for the outside route in the OOD 34 which I was navigating, and many hours later we crossed tacks with another OOD 34 which we had been next to at St Alban's. It later transpired that they had opted for the inshore route, so in that case at least it did not particularly pay to go

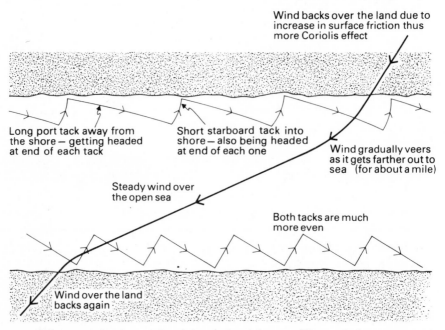

Wind backs over the land due to increase in surface friction thus more Coriolis effect

Long port tack away from the shore — getting headed at end of each tack

Short starboard tack into shore — also being headed at end of each one

Wind gradually veers as it gets farther out to sea (for about a mile)

Steady wind over the open sea

Both tacks are much more even

Wind over the land backs again

9.19 Why to stay by the port-hand shore when it has an offshore wind

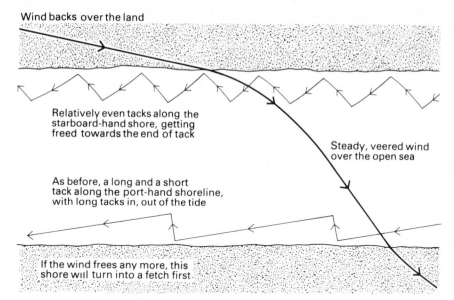

Wind backs over the land

Relatively even tacks along the starboard-hand shore, getting freed towards the end of tack

Steady, veered wind over the open sea

As before, a long and a short tack along the port-hand shoreline, with long tacks in, out of the tide

If the wind frees any more, this shore will turn into a fetch first

9.20 Why to stay on the port-hand shore while beating, when it has an onshore wind

inshore as although we had ended up on the wrong side of a wind shift in the Channel which must have helped the yachts that went inshore, we were level when next we met.

However, if the coastline is there, with less foul tide and no tidal gates threatening, then it is obviously going to be advantageous to use that coast when stemming the tide.

Given an equal choice of two coasts to cheat the tide with, each having similar features, then it will probably be the local effects of each shore on the wind that decide which is going to be more advantageous. As a general rule, the coast that is on the boat's port side will be best from the point of view of land-induced wind bend, as shown in Figs 9.19 and 9.20. The reasons behind these meteorological effects are discussed further in Chapter 11.

Strategy—Close Fetching

When the wind frees to the extent that the next mark can just be laid on one tack, a fairly complicated decision has to be made. Should one sail free and fast, hoping that the wind will not head later, or would it be better to point high initially and then bear away later if the wind remains constant?

Sailing high of the rhumb line Sailing to windward of the rhumb line will rarely pay! Assuming that it is faster to sail freer, then the only occasion when it will pay to sail high initially is if the wind is going to head you a little at some stage during the leg. As can be seen from Fig. 9.21, the exact degree of sailing high that pays needs to be worked out in every situation, as it will depend on the combination of the extra speed attained by sailing freer, the extra distance sailed by going high on the rhumb line, and the magnitude of the wind shift. Unless one is very sure of all these factors and their interrelation, it is nearly always safer not to sail high.

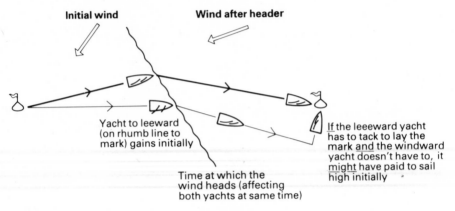

Initial wind

Wind after header

Yacht to leeward
(on rhumb line to
mark) gains initially

If the leeward yacht
has to tack to lay the
mark <u>and</u> the windward
yacht doesn't have to, it
mi<u>ght</u> have paid to sail
high initially

Time at which the
wind heads (affecting
both yachts at same time)

9.21 Sailing high of the rhumb line when close-fetching

Sailing to leeward of the rhumb line It is probably easiest to consider the three main possibilities separately.

(1) Wind remains constant: if it is assumed that the mark could only just be laid by sailing along the rhumb line, then if a boat sails to leeward of the rhumb line to start with she is bound to have to tack in order to lay the mark if the wind remains constant. The extra distance necessitated by the tack onto the unfavoured tack then has to be com-

$$AC = \text{rhumb line distance}$$
$$AB + BC = \text{distance travelled to same point if sailing below rhumb line by angle } \mathbf{a}$$
$$(AB + BC) - AC = \text{extra distance}$$
$$\frac{(AB + BC) - AC}{AC} \times 100 = \% \text{ increase in speed required to justify sailing this low}$$

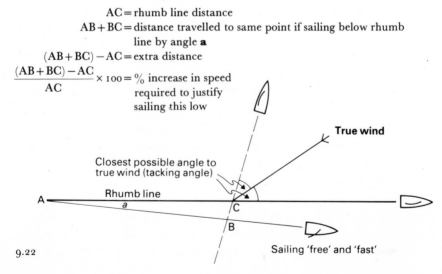

True wind

Closest possible angle to
true wind (tacking angle)

Rhumb line

A ——— *a* ——— C

B

9.22

Sailing 'free' and 'fast'

pensated for by an increase in speed. If the tacking angle of the yacht is known this can be calculated as shown in Fig. 9.22. However, if the rhumb line gives the best Vmg then this will obviously never pay, but with small angles to leeward of the rhumb line the losses incurred will also be small.

(2) Wind frees: if the wind frees enough so that the mark can be laid from the leeward position then it will have paid to sail to leeward to start with.

(3) Wind heads: if the boat has sailed to leeward and the wind heads her, then it is the size of the header which will determine whether or not the faster initial course was good. A small header which still enables the yacht to windward to lay the mark but prevents the leeward yacht from doing so will favour the windward yacht, whereas a larger header which prevents either from laying the mark will tend to favour the leeward yacht. The larger the header, the more the leeward yacht will have gained by sailing faster before the wind shifted.

So, on a long leg when one cannot be certain of the wind remaining constant, it will very often pay to sail to leeward of the rhumb line by a few degrees as long as this will significantly increase boat speed. Where there are a few degrees in hand it will almost certainly pay to sail faster to leeward of the rhumb line, at least until the point is reached where the mark can only just be laid, as this is in effect the same as the wind freeing from an initial point of only just being able to lay the mark.

Reaching Strategy

The strategy employed on a reaching leg needs to be related very closely to polar speed diagrams or the equivalent. Assuming that the next mark can be laid even from a position well to leeward of the rhumb line, one needs to compare the distances sailed together with the speeds attained for different angles to the wind and thus calculate which combination of courses give the fastest overall result.

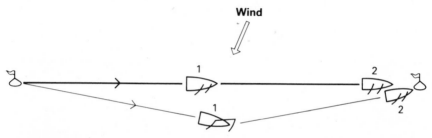

9.23 Sailing a longer course to carry a spinnaker, when the speed gain offsets the greater distance covered. The yachts' positions at (1) and (2) show how far each has sailed in the same time.

As a general principle, if one is close to the angle for a significant jump in speed (e.g. able to surf, hoist a spinnaker, etc) then it will probably be worth bearing away to get that increase, at least at the start of the leg. It should soon become apparent from observation if the actual increase in speed is worth the extra distance sailed. This technique of sailing low initially is shown in Fig. 9.23; in this example it is assumed that there will be a 15 per cent increase in speed when the spinnaker is set, and that without a spinnaker reaching is at about the same speed regardless of wind angle. This is obviously simplifying the case since even two-sail reaching will vary in speed somewhat as wind angle changes (especially for multihulls), but it serves to exemplify the problem.

If, on the other hand, no such dramatic increase in speed is possible by bearing away a little, then it will normally pay to stay near to the rhumb line.

When sailing in tidal waters it can be worthwhile calculating the effect of an impending change in the stream on the apparent wind strength and direction. For example it may be best to sail low while the tide is against the lee side (lee-bowing), pushing the yacht up to windward and increasing the apparent wind, and then head up again when the tide turns onto the other side with a corresponding decrease in the apparent wind strength and reduction of speed at larger angles to the wind.

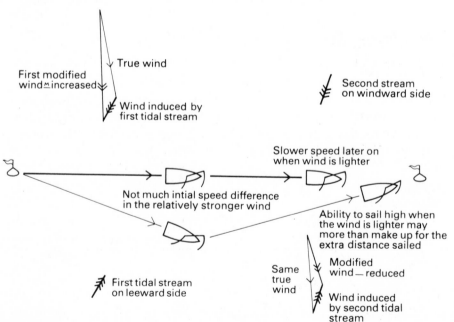

9.24 Reaching strategy with a changing cross-tide

If sailing nearly into a foul tide, take care to ensure that the yacht is not inadvertently set sideways by the tidal stream, by having headed up or borne away from the rhumb line a little (Fig. 9.25).

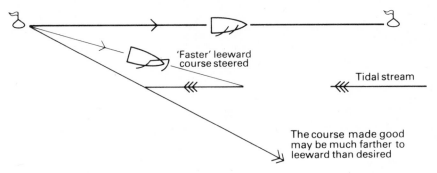

9.25 Reaching against the current

Running Strategy

Downwind tacking In a tideless situation the strategy required on a running leg of the course is quite simple. As was shown in Chapter 5, the speed of a yacht falls off rapidly as a dead run is approached, except in very strong winds, and thus one should normally tack downwind (Fig. 9.26). The ideal tacking angle will obviously depend on the percentage speed increase compared to the percentage extra distance sailed. Ideally this increase would be found from a speed polar diagram for the particular yacht as this enables the tacking angle to be calculated rather than having to be worked out by trial and error during the race. With speed polar diagrams for different wind strengths, the optimum downwind tacking angle can be worked out beforehand for each wind strength and this information can be used in conjunction with a sail change polar diagram to show which sails should give the best results. However, if all this data is not available then you have little option but to experiment at the time by gradually heading up from the run while noting any increase in speed. Using Appendix 3 you can compare the increase in speed with the tacking angle and see immediately whether it is good or bad.

If the downwind tacking angle table given in Appendix 3 is studied, it will be appreciated that while small tacking angles, say up to 10°, will nearly always pay because the speed increases needed to justify them are so small, larger tacking angles are only likely to pay in light winds. Even in light winds (and thus lower overall speeds), when one gets much above 30° from a dead run the speed increases needed to justify another 5° off course rapidly get much larger.

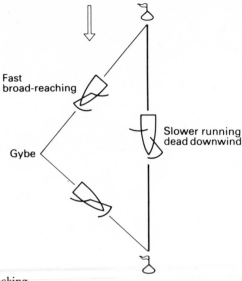

9.26 Downwind tacking

Final gybe to the mark As was shown in Chapter 8, with no stream and with the speed of the yacht at about the speed of the apparent wind, the layline for the leeward mark will be reached when the Windex indicator or the burgee is pointing at the mark. The reasons behind this have already been fully discussed, but Fig. 9.27 illustrates the point.

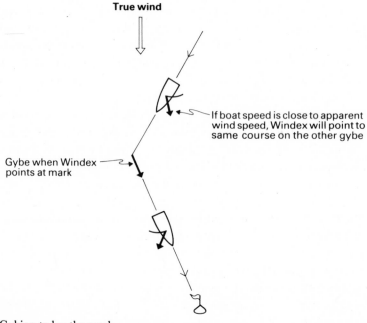

9.27 Gybing to lay the mark

Downwind tacking with wind shifts A point often overlooked is that the wind is just as likely to change direction while one is sailing downwind as it is when sailing upwind. Wind shifts can be utilised on the run in exactly the same way that they were while beating, to give a favoured tack or in this case a favoured 'gybe'. Fig. 9.28 shows the principle involved.

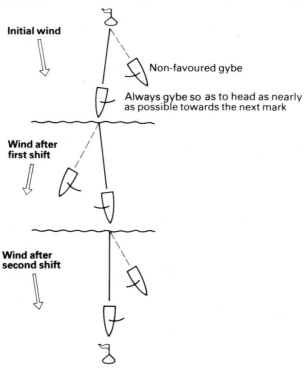

9.28 Downwind tacking on wind shifts

Since the basis for deciding when to gybe on the run is so similar to the timing of tacks upwind, it follows that the same sort of procedures can usefully be employed in making these decisions.

Use of sectors Although we have seen that the actual tacking angle which has the optimum Vmg can be calculated, how far to go on each gybe still has to be decided. On long legs sectors can be used to limit each gybe so that one is not caught too far away from a line dead up-wind from the mark by a wind shift. As the tacking angles likely to be used in downwind sailing are so much smaller than those needed upwind, the sectors should be smaller too: a 5° sector is probably about right unless one is gybing through angles of more than about 30°. The size of sector will depend on the boat's ideal downwind tacking angle at the time: a larger angle means a wider sector, up to about 10° maximum.

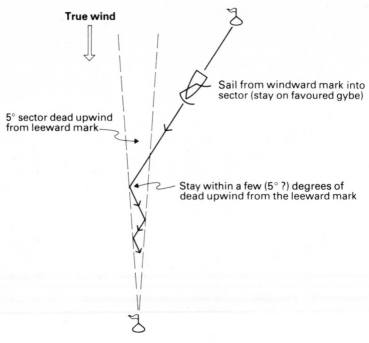

True wind

Sail from windward mark into
sector (stay on favoured gybe)

5° sector dead upwind
from leeward mark

Stay within a few (5° ?) degrees of
dead upwind from the leeward mark

9.29 Use of sectors in downwind tacking

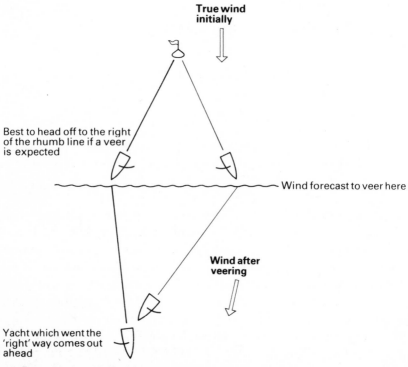

True wind
initially

Best to head off to the right
of the rhumb line if a veer
is expected

Wind forecast to veer here

Wind after
veering

Yacht which went the
'right' way comes out
ahead

9.30 Downwind tacking with an expected wind shift

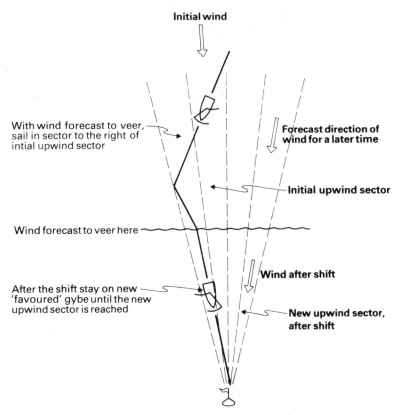

Initial wind

With wind forecast to veer, sail in sector to the right of intial upwind sector

Forecast direction of wind for a later time

Initial upwind sector

Wind forecast to veer here

Wind after shift

After the shift stay on new 'favoured' gybe until the new upwind sector is reached

New upwind sector, after shift

9.31 Tacking downwind when a wind shift is forecast

Expected shifts If the wind is forecast to change direction by either veering or backing, then you should gybe away from the expected shift, i.e. to the right of the rhumb line if the wind is forecast to veer and to the left of the rhumb line if the wind is likely to back (Fig. 9.30).

Unless the exact amount of wind shift can be forecast, it will still pay to sail in sectors thus limiting any losses incurred due to the shift not happening as expected. If the wind is forecast to veer, then the sector to the right of the initial dead upwind sector should be used (Fig. 9.31), and conversely if the wind is expected to back.

Downwind tacking in a steady cross-tide On a running leg of the course with a steady current or tidal stream, sectors can still be used to limit the distance travelled away from the rhumb line. However, the sectors used must take into account both the 'modified' wind direction and the courses and distances made good over the ground on each gybe. This means that before the appropriate sector can be chosen, these vectors of course/distance made good have to be calculated, as shown in Fig. 9.32.

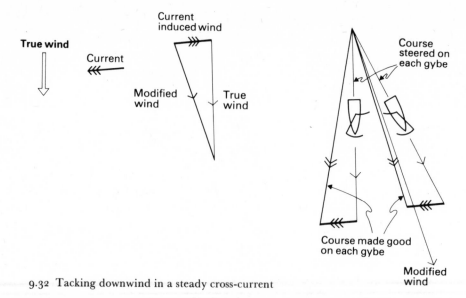

9.32 Tacking downwind in a steady cross-current

The resultant of these two vectors then forms the centre of the sector upwind of the mark. So, assuming that it is known that the current rate and direction will remain steady for the whole of the run downwind, you should sail from the windward mark into this sector and then use it for limiting each gybe as if there was no current (Fig. 9.33).

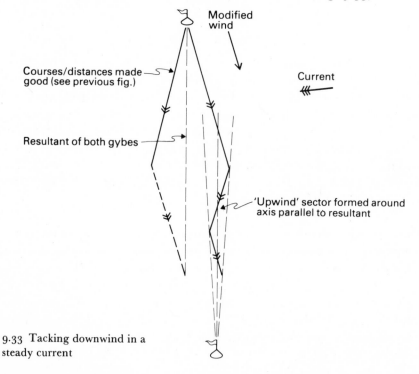

9.33 Tacking downwind in a steady current

Downwind tacking with a changing cross-tide If the stream is going to change direction during a running leg of the course, then obviously the modified wind direction will also change direction. This fact can be used to advantage when tacking downwind just as it can when beating upwind. However, the advantages to be gained downwind will not be nearly as large as those which are possible upwind since the change in direction of the modified wind will be countered to some extent by the tidal drift. Once again it is the vectors of course and distance made good which are relevant, and not merely the courses steered. The effect of the change in tidal stream direction on course steered can be seen in Fig. 9.34 while an example of the total effect of the change on the course made good is shown in Fig. 9.35.

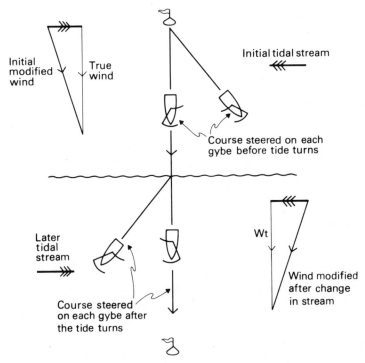

9.34 Effect of change in tidal stream direction on the course steered downwind

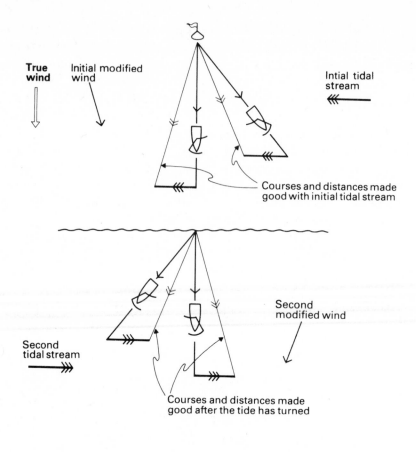

True wind　Initial modified wind

Intial tidal stream

Courses and distances made good with initial tidal stream

Second modified wind

Second tidal stream

Courses and distances made good after the tide has turned

9.35 Effect of change in stream direction on course made good downwind

Running with or against the stream If the current or tidal stream is more or less in the same line as the true wind, then a change in the stream rate will not modify the direction of the wind very much. It will, however, affect the strength of the wind, wind-against-tide giving an increase in wind strength and vice-versa when the wind is with the tide. (There may also be a definite change in the size and steepness of waves, affecting the boat's motion, and thus influencing sail selection.)

Chapter 10 **Inshore Races**

Factors Common to Most Inshore Races

As a general rule, navigation in the normal sense of the word becomes less and less important as races become shorter. However, this does not mean that navigation is not required, merely that the emphasis and type of navigation needs to change. For example, transits become more important than shaping courses to steer, and echo-sounder readings are more valuable than radio direction-finding.

Tactics versus strategy On short courses there is almost bound to be more close boat-to-boat racing than on a long offshore race and this means that tactics play a more important role in inshore races than they do offshore. It is very often more important to stay in clear air or to ensure an inside overlap at the next mark than it is to sail along pre-determined courses. Having said that, though, it is also important not to go too far along the tactical road. One must have worked out a course along with a navigational strategy to go with it before it can be determined that the tactics are more important and should over-ride it. Without a strategy worked out it is possible to be forced into making silly errors just to cover another boat that might also be making the same errors!

Mark rounding inshore This is one of the classic situations that was being referred to in the paragraph above. Because the boats all congregate, it is also a very important time to get the boat-to-boat tactics correct and this very often leads to whole groups all doing the same wrong thing, especially just after the mark. If the next mark can be seen when the present one is being rounded, then it is obviously more accurate to steer either along a transit to reach it or to maintain a compass bearing (with the hand bearing compass) relative to it rather than sailing along a previously worked out course to steer. However, both of these methods of deciding the course to steer involve trial and error in that an approximate course has to be steered before the transit or compass bearing can be settled on. It is therefore far better, and nearly always worthwhile, to shape a course to steer before the mark is reached, give the helmsman this course as a starter, and find a transit or whatever once the boat has settled on the new leg. This enables the helmsman to concentrate on the tactical considerations when rounding the mark while still knowing what sort of course he needs to steer.

Apparent wind calculations The calculation of the new apparent wind for the next leg of the course (Chapter 8) is even more important in short races than in long offshore races. If the next leg is 60 miles long, the percentage of the total time lost by being wrong in the initial choice of sails with a subsequent sail change being needed is very small, whereas if the next leg is only a mile then having to do a sailchange because of a wrong decision is probably catastrophic. The fact that the new course to steer has to be known before the new apparent wind can be calculated is yet another argument in favour of always working out a course before the buoy is reached.

Identification of the next mark Offshore race marks are normally large and easily identifiable, but in inshore racing they are very often small and look similar to other marks in the vicinity. This means that positive identification is vital since it is very embarrassing to be going around the wrong marks. It is always worth ensuring that the buoys being used are all marked on the chart in their correct positions and with the right symbols. On Admiralty (and probably other) charts, nearly all buoys used for racing as opposed to navigation will just be marked as 'orange' and probably as 'spherical' regardless of whether they are actually orange or yellow and whether they have identifying marks etc. If they are precisely indicated on the chart the problems of identification are much reduced.

As well as knowing the course to steer from one mark to the next, it is also worth knowing the actual bearing of the next mark as well so that as a mark is rounded, or even as it is approached, the hand bearing compass can be used to look in the right direction for the next buoy. This is one instance where the type of compass that is incorporated into binoculars or a monocular can be very useful. The same technique of using a hand bearing compass to look in the direction of the next mark can also be used from a fix halfway along the leg if the buoy was not visible from the previous mark.

Tidal heights In Chapter 4 on pre-race planning it was stated that it is worth calculating the height of the tide for any parts of the race where the course may take you close to land. In inshore races, almost by definition the whole course is likely to be close to land and therefore the tidal heights should be calculated for the whole race. In areas where there is little difference in the Secondary Port corrections from one end of the course to the other this will present few difficulties, but sometimes it can involve a large number of calculations. If a calculator is being used, particularly one with a paper printout, it may well be best to use the Admiralty method of tidal prediction using harmonic constants to get a printout for the day for each Secondary Port involved. If a fully programmable calculator is not available then it is probably easiest to work from the normal tidal curves to get the data for each hour. As well as working out the height of the tide above chart datum, it is also feasible and sometimes valuable to work out the actual depths of water over various charted rocks and shallows for the estimated time of passing close to them. This enables a very rapid appraisal of when and whether it is safe to go over a particular shallow patch, and also it allows one to calculate (and mark on the chart) when particular rocks will be exposed and visible as fixing marks.

Tidal streams Just as it is possible to consider the tidal heights in more detail in an inshore (short) race, so it is also feasible to look at the tidal streams in more detail. The tidal streams for at least the first (or next) leg of the course should be memorised, taking into account the range of the tide for the day and looking at the likelihood of any counter-currents, inshore eddies etc.

Echo-sounding As a navigational aid offshore the echo-sounder is distinctly limited in use, but inshore it is probably the most valuable single aid. It can either be used in conjunction with a knowledge of the charted depths and the predicted tidal heights or it can be used in its own right. It is most common to use the echo-sounder in the latter mode, merely watching it and heading away from the shore or shallows when the depth reaches a predetermined minimum, or heading back inshore when deep water is reached. The only difficult thing here is knowing at what sort of rate the depth is going to change, by having an appreciation of what the seabed contours look like. In basic terms this can be done without reference to tidal heights, but a more accurate picture can be built up if the tidal heights are known as well. As a general principle it is normally better if the helmsman *cannot* see the echo-sounder as the yacht heads for the shore as the worry about depth is bound to distract him from steering a fast course. However, a large amount of trust is called for if the navigator is going to call the shots completely on where to tack, and so a common compromise is to have someone (not necessarily the navigator) calling out the depths for interpretation by the helmsman. If this system is used then it is vital that the terminology being used is understood precisely by all concerned. I will normally call the depths out every 2 or 3 metres until down to 10 metres or so, and then call more frequently after that. I will also give an indication of the rate of change for example 'Nine metres, slowly shelving', or 'Seven metres, shelving rapidly', or if the bottom is really coming up fast, just 'Tack!'. If misunderstandings are not to happen, this final request should only be used when it is really meant. If I know what the type of bottom is, I will also give an indication of this when I am calling out the depths, so that the helmsman knows whether he is going in towards rock, where one set of safety margins might come into play, or towards mud, when safety margins can be much smaller.

The other way to utilise an echo-sounder is to know what the change in depth at a particular point should be and to decide from the actual depth at an earlier place whether it will be possible to get over the shallows or not. In cases where the safety margins are very small this can be a more accurate way of predicting depths than using tide tables since it automatically takes into account the meteorological effects of the day on the time and height of the tide whereas the tide tables clearly cannot do this.

Fixing position On short inshore races there is very often no need to fix the position except in a purely visual manner, merely looking around and saying 'we're more or less . . . here'. However, there will be times when an accurate position related to the chart is needed, for example to know which side of a particular underwater rock you are going, or in bad visibility or at night. When an actual fix is required it is likely that it will need to be much more accurate than the average fix taken on an offshore race, where errors of a hundred metres are irrelevant. There is nothing magic in obtaining really accurate fixes, just an awareness of what is required. Objects used for fixing should be as near as possible, and whenever feasible transits should be used in preference to compass bearings. If a particular inshore area is going to be raced on very often then it can be time well spent to chart for oneself the positions of useful fixing objects. Such landmarks as a particular house, beach hut, lamp-post etc can all become charted objects to enable a fix (or perhaps a leading line or clearing bearing) to be obtained in places where it would otherwise be difficult or impossible.

Clearing bearings It is inshore that a clearing bearing will most often be valuable (these were mentioned in Chapter 3 on basic techniques). There is often not enough time to get an actual fix before a decision has to be taken as to whether a danger is going to be cleared safely or not; also, a fix is out of date as soon as it has been taken as the yacht is always moving. Thus to have clearing bearings (or even better, transits) to take one around a danger is a really easy way to navigate. Because the safety line can be worked out accurately beforehand with the tidal height and charted depth all taken into account, the margins for safety can be significantly reduced compared to attempting to fix one's position at the time, and thus a few more yards can be saved and more places gained.

Local meteorology This is discussed in some detail in Chapter 11. Suffice to say here that if racing inshore, obviously the effects of the land on the wind will be more important than when sailing largely offshore.

Olympic Triangle Courses

An 'Olympic' type of course is very often used for inshore races or in championships. As Fig. 10.1 shows, the course is basically triangular with its long leg being dead upwind. A complete race will normally consist of the following sequence. An upwind start and a beat to the first turning mark, a broad reach to the second mark, a gybe and another broad reach to the leeward (third) mark. This completes the triangle and may be called lap 1. A beat around the windward mark and a run down to the leeward mark is the second lap; it is followed by a final beat up to the finish line. Or, as it's sometimes summed up, 'a triangle, a sausage and a beat to the finish'.

To avoid right-of-way problems at the windward mark, the course

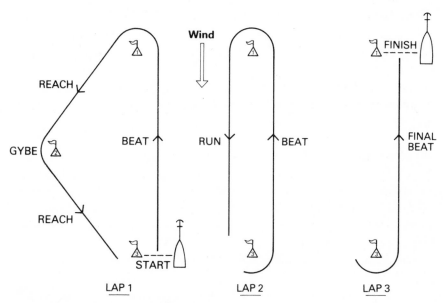

10.1 A typical 'Olympic' triangle course

will nearly always be set so as to leave all turning marks to port. Because of this and because the buoys should all be laid in relation to the wind direction, it is usually possible to select the sails which will be used for the downwind legs long before the marks are reached and also get set up for the gybe early (perhaps even before the start of the race).

Checking for wind shifts Since the first leg will always be to windward and is likely to be only a few miles long (2 or 3 miles would be quite normal) it is feasible to sail up the beat before the start and check for wind bends and consistency in wind shifts. If the course has been set near a headland, for example, it may well pay handsomely to sail the beats very much on one side to take advantage of the effect that the headland has on the wind.

Tidal streams For an Olympic type of course to be successful, it should ideally be set in an area of weak and, if possible consistent, tides so that the streams experienced by the leaders are the same as those affecting yachts farther down the fleet. In the ideal situation the tidal streams will not play an important part in a race of this type. However, it is quite common for a certain amount of compromise to have been made in the choice of sailing area in the interests of convenience or tradition, and so it is always worth studying the streams and currents that are likely to affect the sailing area in case advantage can be gained.

If a campaign is being taken seriously and it involves Olympic triangle courses, then homework before the start of a series will nearly always pay off. Just to stand on headlands around the course area and watch boats sailing can tell you a lot about how the local geography affects the wind, and by either sailing in the course area or hiring a motorboat and sitting at anchor at strategic places, a lot can be learned about the timing and direction of tidal streams and currents. If you want to win in an area where no-one on the boat has detailed local knowledge, then such reconnaissance is vital.

Navigating around an Olympic course Assuming the course has been laid in a basically suitable area with weak tides, the actual process of navigating should be fairly minimal. Indeed, quite a lot of top boats will replace their navigator in this type of racing with a tactician as it is boat-to-boat tactics which play a more important role. The navigation will consist of:

(1) At the start, deciding which end of the line to start and doing the timing.

(2) Up the beat, watching for wind shifts and deciding whether they are worth tacking on, and deciding when to tack so as to lay the mark.

(3) Calculating the apparent wind strength and direction for each leg and thus getting the sail choice correct.

(4) Working out a basic course for the downwind legs. This needn't necessarily be very precise as the other competitors are likely to force deviations from the desired course in order to maintain clear air.

(5) Calculating the yacht's position on handicap before the final beat, to know whether it is best to conserve one's position by covering or whether it would possibly be better to take a bit of a flyer or whatever in order to attempt to improve one's place. This will be particularly important in a series where the combined result of all the races in the series is more important than the result of an individual race.

(6) On the run, it will obviously be necessary to decide on the downwind tacking angle for maximum Vmg and watch for wind shifts to enable this angle to be maintained with least distance sailed.

Racing in the Solent

Of all the inshore racing around the British Isles, the Solent is undoubtedly the most crowded and overused stretch of water imaginable. Although there are many other major centres of inshore racing, the number of yachts racing in the Solent probably outnumbers all the rest put together, hence this section treating it in detail. Apart from its location, relatively close to London and the Midlands, it is without doubt the shelter offered by the Isle of Wight which makes it so popular. It is also the Isle of Wight which makes it an especially difficult place to race without local knowledge: the tidal streams are complex and fairly strong and the local meteorological effects are made more complicated by the existence of two coastlines within a few miles of each other.

Tidal streams in the Solent Anyone hoping to win races in the Solent must have a copy of the Admiralty tidal stream atlas *Solent and Adjacent Waters* before he can even start. This shows that the main flood tide runs from west to east, but that because of the water coming around the south of the Island the tidal streams turn between 1 and $1\frac{1}{2}$ hours before the top of the tide (high water). It can thus be a dangerous misconception to think of the tidal streams in relation to the flood or ebb; it is far safer to merely consider the stream as being either west-going or east-going as one fact and then to think of the tidal height separately.

Counter-currents Because of the generally strong tidal streams and the large number of headlands, rivers, inlets, etc there are many places in the Solent where there is a counter-current at some stages of the tide. The major ones are shown in some detail on the Admiralty tidal stream atlas, but obviously the smaller eddies and swirls cannot be shown in such a relatively small scale. For the area immediately around Cowes there is a large-scale tidal stream atlas, available locally. This doesn't attempt to quantify the counter-currents in anything more than vague terms, but it does show when the various eddies are likely to start and finish and whether they are strong or weak. It is another essential publication for those sailing around Cowes.

There are also counter-currents in places other than Cowes, notably the following (the High Water referred to is HW Portsmouth in all cases).

IN OSBORNE BAY The general streams are fairly weak here and the tide turns close inshore sooner than in the main channel, sometimes by as much as an hour earlier. Off Wootton Creek in the centre of the Bay it is possible to get quite a strong northerly set as the water comes out of the river. This starts at about 1½ hours after High Water.

IN THE NORTH CHANNEL OUT OF SOUTHAMPTON WATER The stream runs eastwards for 8 hours in 13, turning to the east at about 3 hours after High Water Portsmouth.

IN PORTSMOUTH HARBOUR APPROACHES Due to the stream entering the harbour itself, it is quite often possible to get a fair stream when coming into the Solent from the east by sailing up the first part of the main harbour channel, before cutting across the relatively slack water over the Hamilton Bank area to Gilkicker Point. This effect can be used to advantage from 6 hours after High Water until about 2 hours before the next high tide.

BETWEEN BEMBRIDGE AND THE SOLENT PROPER Close inshore along this coast there are very often counter-currents, or at least areas of slack water. There is also great variation in the rate of the tidal stream in the main channel, particularly with the east-going tide. It is quite common to see bands of faster flowing water and if these are looked for they can be utilised.

IN THE WESTERN SOLENT There are fewer counter-currents as such in the main part of the Western Solent, but there are very great differences in the rate of the stream depending on exactly where one is at a particular time. As a general principle the streams on the north (mainland) shore are considerably less than the corresponding stream on the Island shore. This is due to the gently shelving shoreline on the mainland side where it is possible to sail relatively far out of the main channel, compared to the predominantly steep-shelving Island coastline where one is forced to sail in deep water most of the time.

Two notable places in the Western Solent where there is a counter-current are GURNARD BAY and THORNESS BAY. In both of these bays, but particularly in Gurnard Bay, the stream tends to turn at least an hour before the stream in the main channel.

HURST NARROWS Another place where the tide is both critical and complicated. In behind the peninsula itself there is nearly always *relatively* slack water, and in general the closer one gets to either shore the slacker the stream will tend to be; indeed on the Island shore there is sometimes a counter-current at least as far as Fort Victoria. Thus happens especially at spring tides and can give an east-going stream to to $1\frac{1}{2}$ hours before the overall turn of the tide.

OVER THE SHINGLE BANK There are not, so far as I am aware, any counter-currents over the Shingle Bank, but it is worth noting that on the west-going tide the stream sets strongly over the bank and is strongest at the point where the water starts to shallow.

IN BEAULIEU RIVER As the tide turns westwards in the Western Solent at about $1-1\frac{1}{2}$ hours before High Water, the stream in the River at this time will still just be flooding. From this time until about 1 or possibly 2 hours after high water it may be worth considering entering Beaulieu River via Needs Oar Channel if sailing against the main west-going stream. This can be particularly useful if running against the tide with very light winds and is obviously more feasible for shallow draft yachts. As a guide to the depth in the entrance, if all the mud around the entrance is covered, leaving only the grassy tops of the banks exposed, then there is at least 2 metres of water through the middle of the entrance. At least there was in 1982. . . .

Negotiating particularly tricky rocks and headlands There are a number of strategically important areas in the Solent where local knowledge is needed as a supplement to the normally excellent Admiralty charts (even though these are to the scale of 1:20,000). The following notes may prove helpful to those who do not possess the necessary local knowledge. However, they should be used with some caution as the shallow areas do tend to move slightly over the years.

BRAMBLES BANK This bank, at the entrance to Southampton Water, is where more yachts end up aground than probably anywhere else in the Solent. It consists of clean hard sand and its southern edge in particular is very steep-to. There is a post marking the extreme southeasterly corner of the bank, but the shallowest part is at present near the westerly corner where it dries to about 1.3 metres above chart datum. The northern boundary of the bank is well marked by the small West Knoll buoy and a line between West and East Knoll buoys will

keep one clear of the bank. At the right state of the tide it is possible to
sail over the top of the Brambles, and when calculating the tidal height
to determine the feasibility of this Calshot Spit is as good a Secondary
Port to use as any other.

STANSORE (STONE) POINT A headland just to the east of Beaulieu River
entrance and important because of the strength of the tidal streams
around it. It is easy to identify the Point as it has three off-lying beacons
marking power cables (red and white diamond-shaped topmarks on
piles, lit by Q Fl Red lights visible about a mile). Between the beacons
and the shore there is a shingle bank, parts of which dry to about 2
metres, and at any time around Low Water it is safest to stay on the
line of, or just outside, the beacons. With sufficient tidal height it is
possible to go either inside the beacons by 20 to 30 metres keeping just
outside the shingle bank, or through an inshore channel as shown in
Fig. 10.2.

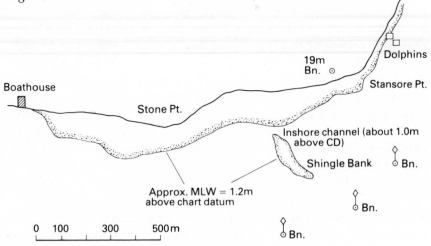

10.2 Sketch of Stansore and Stone Points

GURNARD LEDGE Another bank which it is very often possible to pass
inside of, but very steep-to and composed of rocks. The shallowest part
of the ledge is charted as drying 0.2 metres and there is a deep scoured-
out channel inside of about 5.0 metres at CD. This channel is entered
at either end by going over a relatively shallow patch with about 0.5
metres of water at CD. In places the deep channel is only 40 metres
wide and over the Ledge itself the tide still runs very quickly, but with
care (and a good echo-sounder) it is possible to gain a few metres by
going inside the Ledge.

THORNESS BAY Having rounded Quarry Ledge, which comes up
incredibly steeply, it is possible to carry on into Thorness Bay for a

surprising distance. The seabed in the bay is nearly all flat, with just a few isolated rocks which are all well charted. Apart from the advantage of getting out of the main tidal stream there is also a significant wind shift as one goes into the bay with a southwesterly wind. Standing in towards the shore on starboard tack, one is headed quite sharply and it is then possible to flip onto port and be freed by as much as 10° or 15° compared to yachts only a hundred metres or so outside.

NEWTOWN GRAVEL BANKS I mention these gravel banks mainly because I was lured into spending ten minutes aground on them during one Cowes Week. The temptation is there because as one approaches from the east there is a deep patch (about 6 metres) just to the west of Saltmead Ledge where one is perfectly safe, but then the gravel banks come out quite quickly and if sailing parallel to the coast (using the wind bend near the land) it is easy to end up 50 metres too close to the shore.

OSBORNE BAY The only problems in Osborne Bay are the isolated rocks making up West and East Patches (charted), both of which I have found with a keel at one time or another, and the really fluky winds around Old Castle Point. Here the temptation is to stand right in to the shore, knowing that there is enough depth and hoping to get out of the tide, only to find that there is no wind at all and yachts farther out are travelling much faster. Unless the wind is blowing parallel to the coast, it is rarely worth going closer than about 100 metres to the headland.

RYDE SANDS A very large expanse of sand most of which is nearly flat. The SW Mining Ground buoy marks its northern extremity (lying 50 metres off the bank) and it is also marked by a couple of red piles. The northeastern end of the bank dries to about 1.7 metres but as one gets to the west of the Mining Ground buoy the bank only dries to 0.7 metres, and this extra metre of water can enable one to go inshore by as much as a quarter of a mile. Over the bank itself the tidal streams are much weaker than in the main channel, but on the edges of the bank the streams are still strong.

Solent meteorology Because it is surrounded by land, the local weather can get very complicated, particularly in anti-cyclonic conditions when sea breezes may predominate.

As the land starts to heat up the sea breezes will start all around the Solent, being caused initially by the Island as well as the mainland. Thus in mid-morning it is possible to get a northerly breeze on the Island shore and a southerly one near the mainland. As the day progresses, though, the mainland normally takes over and the early northerly breezes die out, giving way to a basically southerly sea breeze. In the Western Solent it will actually start more SSW whereas in the Eastern Solent it will be SSE: this very often means that the area off Old Castle Point (near Cowes) has no wind at all since the two opposing winds meet here. By mid-afternoon the Coriolis force will have swung the wind more to the west, and often the sea breeze from the Western Solent over-rides that in the East to give a westerly wind for the late afternoon and early evening all over the Solent.

A second effect is that of wind bend due to the Island. As is explained in Chapter 11, wind is backed more over the land than over the sea because of the extra friction. With the prevailing southwesterly winds this fact can be very important in the Solent as the wind is very often blowing off the Island shore. With a south to southwest wind then, yachts beating down the Solent (especially the Western Solent) will be significantly freed on port tack if the Island shore is kept to, and thus it will very often pay to keep to the Island side with a long port tack and a short board on starboard especially if beating with the tide.

Chapter 11 **Meteorology**

Local Weather

While the large weather systems are of obvious importance to the racing navigator in relation to long-term strategy, it is often an understanding of smaller-scale and more local effects that a coastline or cloud can have on the wind that wins races.

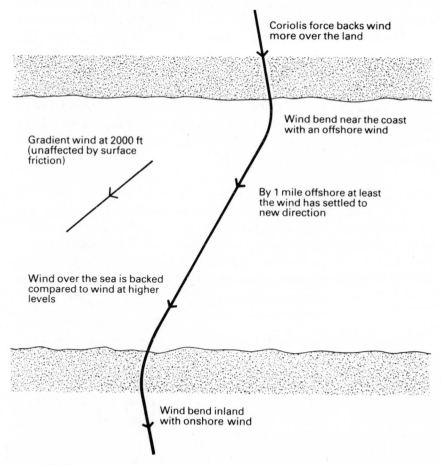

Coriolis force backs wind
more over the land

Wind bend near the coast
with an offshore wind

Gradient wind at 2000 ft
(unaffected by surface
friction)

By 1 mile offshore at least
the wind has settled to
new direction

Wind over the sea is backed
compared to wind at higher
levels

Wind bend inland
with onshore wind

11.1 Wind bend at a coastline. The Coriolis effect is reversed in the Southern Hemisphere so the wind veers over the land.

Wind bend at a coastline Every sailor who concentrates must at some time or another have noticed that the wind very often appears to be different as one approaches the shore. While this change may be due to such things as sea breeze or katabatic wind, if the wind being felt is not a purely local one then the most likely explanation is as follows: wind is slowed by friction more over land than over water, and because it has been slowed down it is affected more by the Coriolis force (force due to the spin of the earth) than it would otherwise be. This has the effect of always *backing* the wind over the land compared to the wind over the sea, in the Northern Hemisphere (*veering* in the Southern). So, as one approaches within a mile or so of the coast, if the wind is blowing offshore it will gradually back (NH). This will not happen with an onshore wind as all the wind bend will occur over the land, as shown in Fig. 11.1.

The actual amount of wind bend will depend on several factors. The rougher the terrain, the more the surface wind will have been slowed down and therefore the greater will be the bend. As a general principle lighter winds will be bent more than stronger ones. The sort of maximum shift that you are likely to experience as the land is approached is 15°–20°.

The practical effect of all this is that if you are approaching a coast on port tack then you will be freed as you get closer in, and vice-versa if you are on starboard (in Northern Hemisphere: opposite in Southern).

Wind shifts in gusts The fact that the wind will very often *veer* (opposite in Southern Hemisphere) in a gust is caused by exactly the same factors that cause wind bends near a coast. Most gusts are in fact downdrafts of wind from one or two thousand feet. The reason that such a downdraft (gust) will have a higher wind speed is because the higher the altitude the less surface friction there is to slow the wind down, and

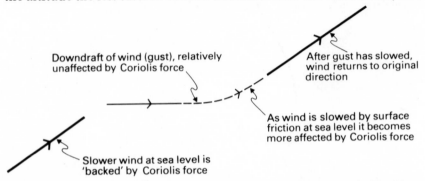

Downdraft of wind (gust), relatively unaffected by Coriolis force

After gust has slowed, wind returns to original direction

As wind is slowed by surface friction at sea level it becomes more affected by Coriolis force

Slower wind at sea level is 'backed' by Coriolis force

11.2 Wind veer in a downdraft gust, seen from above. Again, the opposite bend is found in the Southern Hemisphere.

as we have seen this means that the wind at the surface backs compared with the wind at higher levels.

So, a downdraft is both going faster and in a veered direction relative to the surface wind, and by the time surface friction has slowed the downdraft to the same speed as the surface wind, it isn't a gust any more! This is shown in Fig. 11.2.

Obviously not all gusts are this simple and so the wind will not always veer, but in the absence of evidence to the contrary, if you see a gust coming then it is more likely to veer than to back.

Land topography The effect of a fairly straight coastline on the wind direction has already been described. In a lot of situations, though, the coast will be anything but straight and also the wind may well be blowing more along the coast than either onshore or offshore. Here a different set of guidelines can be followed.

As a general rule, wind is very lazy and will take the easiest path possible. This means that if the wind is blowing along the coast and you put a headland in the way, the wind will tend to go around the headland as well as over it and this will obviously increase the wind speed (strength) at the headland and will probably change its direction as well (Fig. 11.3).

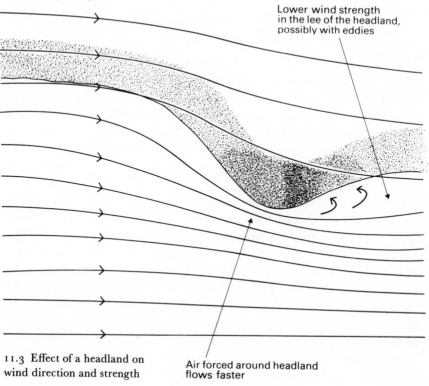

Lower wind strength
in the lee of the headland,
possibly with eddies

11.3 Effect of a headland on
wind direction and strength

Air forced around headland
flows faster

Sea breeze During the summer and within 10 miles or so of the coast the sea breeze phenomenon is probably the most important local weather effect. Although the basic mechanism (Fig. 11.4) is very well known, there are certain complications that cause problems in predicting sea breezes and in understanding what is happening.

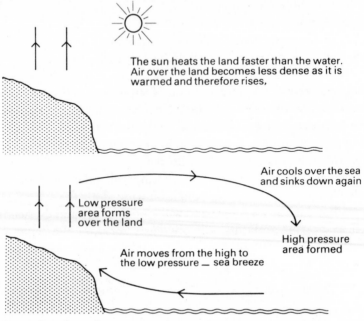

The sun heats the land faster than the water. Air over the land becomes less dense as it is warmed and therefore rises,

Air cools over the sea and sinks down again

Low pressure area forms over the land

High pressure area formed

Air moves from the high to the low pressure — sea breeze

11.4 Formation of a sea breeze

First, as the air over the land rises more moist air is drawn in from over the sea to replace it; this moist air then rises and therefore cools down and forms cumulus clouds. In some cases this is a self-limiting process as the cloud cover formed over the land may stop the land being heated any further, in which case the sea breeze ceases. This will very often be the case if there is no gradient wind to move the clouds away from the coast.

The second complication and major misconception about sea breezes lies in the question of whether an onshore or an offshore wind is more likely to produce the conditions necessary for a good sea breeze. The most commonly held belief is that an onshore wind will help and reinforce a sea breeze generated wind. The second part of Fig. 11.4 shows why this is not so. In order for a sea breeze to become properly established as a circulatory system the drift out to sea of the heated air has to take place, and if there is an onshore wind then this will obviously not happen. In practice an onshore wind will blow the warmed air farther inland and so, although it will be increased very slightly by the land heating up, the effect will not be very great.

To recap, the first two criteria for a good sea breeze are: enough sun to heat the land to a significantly higher temperature than the sea, and an offshore wind to get the circulation started.

The third complication can also be found in the basic sea breeze diagram. For the system even to start, there has to be a difference in the air pressure over the land and sea. As we saw above, the wind backs over the land and veers as it goes over the sea (Northern Hemisphere) In Fig. 11.5 the effect on air pressure can be seen.

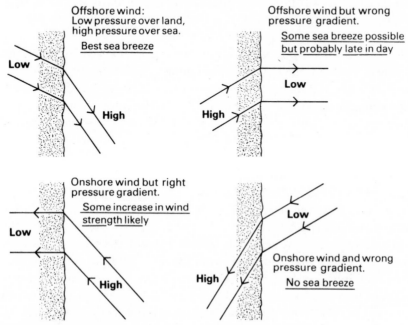

11.5 The effect of gradient wind direction on sea breeze formation

By splitting the direction of the gradient wind into quadrants arranged at right angles to the coast, it is easy to predict whether a good sea breeze is likely on any particular day. This can also be seen in Fig. 11.5. If the gradient wind is in a favourable quadrant and the land is forecast to heat up during the day to 2°C (4°F) or more above the sea temperature, then a sea breeze should set in. If the yacht you are navigating is fitted with a water thermometer (essential in Gulf Stream sailing) then it obviously makes your life even easier.

Fog Although not a phenomenon that is of vital strategic importance to the racing navigator, it is very nice to be able to predict fog *before* you are enveloped in damp greyness. In order to be able to predict it you obviously need to understand why it occurs.

Fog is always caused by the dewpoint of the surface air being reached.

To rephrase that slightly, the warmer the air the more moisture it can absorb, so if air is cooled down there will come a point where it can no longer hold all its moisture as vapour and some will condense out as droplets (viz. bathroom windows). There are many terms for the various reasons for this cooling of air and formation of fog but the two basic mechanisms are as follows.

Advection (sea) Fog is caused by relatively warm moist air coming into contact with relatively cold water. This can either be air that has been heated up over land coming into contact with the sea, or air that has been over warm sea (e.g. the Gulf Stream) coming into contact with colder water (e.g. the Labrador Current).

Radiation Fog is the other major type and is caused by the rapid cooling of the land due to heat radiation into the atmosphere on a clear night. It will not happen out at sea as water doesn't cool down as fast, but having formed over the land this type of fog may then drift 2 or 3 miles out to sea. This can only happen on initially clear nights with a light offshore wind.

Land breeze or offshore breeze Following on from the above, on nights when the land does cool down much more rapidly than the sea it is possible that the reverse of a sea breeze may occur, a circulation being set up due to air being cooled and becoming more dense over the land and drifting out to sea. This will never reach the same intensity or duration as a sea breeze as there is nothing to sustain it once the land has cooled initially. In most cases it is only likely to be around force 1 or 2 and will only occur very close to the shore. It is on nights when radiation fog is formed that land breezes are also likely to happen.

Katabatic winds Along coasts which are very hilly or mountainous katabatic winds are likely and can be quite strong. Basically, the air over higher land will be colder than the air lower down and this colder air will also be denser. It therefore has a tendency to flow downhill and if it can do this uninterrupted, for example down river valleys, then by the time it has reached sea level it may have picked up quite a bit of speed and manifests itself as strong gusts. These can be predicted to some extent and this is important as the katabatic gusts may be in a totally different direction from the gradient wind at the time.

High cliffs and headlands can also cause severe turbulence close inshore and this is often manifested as gusts which can be sudden and quite strong even in otherwise calm conditions.

Weather Forecasts

Depending on where in the world you are sailing, there are many ways of obtaining weather forecasts. What we have looked at so far in this chapter is in effect single-observer forecasting with emphasis on local wind effects, i.e. understanding the principles involved and forecasting for oneself what the wind is going to do. While this is an essential and a very important part of weather forecasting, as there are expert meteorologists all over the world who are working full time at it, it is equally important to know how to use their forecasts to best advantage and in conjunction with one's own observations.

Let us look first at the sources of information available to us as *racing* navigators. Prior to the race starting (up until the 5-minute gun) there are numerous weather services available.

TELEVISION The oceanic weather maps and satellite pictures shown on TV can provide a very clear picture of the major systems that are in force at the time of the start; they also give an excellent basis for drawing your own weather maps during a race.

WEATHER FAX OR CHART RECORDERS If you are lucky enough to have access to a facsimile printer of weather charts then obviously a television set is largely redundant, except for forecasts. However, if your yacht does have such a printer, don't forget that at present they are not allowed to be used *while racing*, except in certain trans-ocean races, nor are TV sets.

TELEPHONE TO WEATHER CENTRES The various public service forecasting centres around the country enable one to speak with meteorologists and discuss in some detail the likely weather for the period of the race.

TELEPHONE TO AIRPORTS Some airport meteorologists are happy to talk to the general public and can be very helpful if not too busy.

COASTGUARD It is possible to call the UK Coastguards on VHF Channel 67 and get reports of the actual weather at their stations, though not forecasts. This can also be done on shore by telephone.

Once the race has actually started, none of the above methods of obtaining weather forecasts and data are at present allowed. In my opinion this should change as accurate weather information is essential to the safety of the yachts racing. The sources of forecasts allowed during a race are limited to radio broadcasts (i.e. transmissions intended for anyone who may be listening) and in the UK they are as follows.

BBC SHIPPING FORECASTS Although severely limited by the BBC in the time allowed, these forecasts contain a wealth of information which enables one to draw fairly accurately a weather map for the whole forecast area. Most of the words used in these forecasts have very precise meanings and if the best is going to be got out of the forecasts then their definitions have to be known. The book entitled *The Yachtsman's Weather Map* by Keith Best and Frank Singleton deals with BBC shipping forecasts in detail; the whole subject of weather and prediction is covered with yachtsmen particularly in mind in *Meteorology at Sea* by Ray Sanderson (pub. Stanford Maritime); he is a Bracknell forecaster responsible for the preparation of shipping forecasts.

The precise times of BBC Shipping Forecasts may change from one year to the next, but *at present* they are broadcast on a frequency of 200 kHz (1500 m) on Radio 4 at 0015, 0625, 1355, 1750. These are obviously not an easy set of times to remember and it is worth having them posted on a bulkhead where they can be easily seen.

INSHORE WATERS FORECASTS Also on BBC Radio 4, this forecast is broadcast after the midnight Shipping Forecast and is primarily intended for inshore fishermen. Because it deals with smaller sea areas, it can on occasions show up small local developments and conditions that have not been included in the main forecast.

LOCAL RADIO Some local radio stations also give weather forecasts (e.g. Radio Bristol, Radio Solent, Radio Medway). They normally concentrate on the land forecast and the inshore waters, so an indication of sea breezes etc can be obtained, and special importance is given to Gale Warnings and strong winds that may be hazardous to small craft.

COAST RADIO STATIONS (e.g. Niton Radio) Around Britain the Coast Radio Stations (operated by British Telecom, ex Post Office) give repeats of Shipping Forecast information at different times, and sometimes information updated since the latest Shipping Forecast, in particular subsequent Gale Warnings. Foreign stations also give marine forecasts and a number of these are repeated in English. *Reed's Almanac* and the Radio Signals Lists give details of the times and frequencies of these forecasts.

Chapter 12 **Errors**

A proper understanding of the sources and magnitudes of errors is essential if you are going to arrive at the right conclusions as navigator. This chapter looks at these errors and discusses how to deal with them so as to minimize their importance.

Distance Run

In average conditions the errors that occur in your estimation of distance run should be fairly small. An adjusted and calibrated log should be accurate to a very small percentage on the distance run side, although the speed readout may well be far more misleading. The exact error will obviously depend on the make of instrument, how well it has been maintained, where it is sited on the hull, etc but an error of 2–3 per cent might be expected. As the regular navigator on a particular boat you will soon get to know your log anyway (so long as no-one 'plays' with the calibration).

In very light conditions when the crew are struggling to get the boat moving at all, the log is probably going to be at its least accurate in percentage terms; but normally it matters far less as the actual distances involved are relatively so small. If the calm conditions carry on for any length of time, though, even the small distances travelled can obviously build up. There is not a lot that you can do to minimize this low-speed error, but to be aware of it is vital. When the speed has dropped so low that the log is not even turning over it can be useful to watch how fast the boat moves away from the inevitable flotsam of beer cans, etc to get an idea of the rate of progress.

At the other end of the speed range, in heavy weather, another set of errors comes into play. To start with, the log will be recording the movement of the boat up and down the waves as well as in a horizontal direction. Unless the waves are unusually steep this error will probably only be in the order of another couple of per cent of total distance (see Chapter 9 on extra distance covered in downwind tacking for an explanation of this). A far bigger error will build up if the boat is surfing on the wave crests as large distances can be covered very rapidly with hardly any motion relative to the wave crest. This error can actually be seen happening if you watch the speedometer while surfing. The maximum recorded speeds probably occur just before a surf with the speed dropping dramatically on the dial as the boat surges forward on the wave. Once again this is a difficult error to quantify, but it may be in the order of 20–100 metres per surf! Even without surfing, there is a small net movement to leeward of the water surface, which will also not register as it carries the boat with it.

The last major source of distance run error is caused by going too fast: this is due to a buildup of nearly static water at the boundary between hull and water. It is a particular problem with the type of impellers that are nearly flush with the surface of the hull, such as paddlewheel impellers. At speeds significantly below the 'hull speed' the boundary layer is very thin, but it gets thicker as speed increases and unless the impeller projects into the water beyond this layer errors of up to 10 per cent may be experienced.

To sum up the errors likely to be inherent in distance run calculations, the order of magnitude will probably be 2–3 per cent in moderate conditions, between 5 and 15 per cent in rough weather, and up to 100 per cent in *very* light winds.

Course Steered

Whereas with distance run we were looking at errors in terms of percentages of the total distance, with errors in the course it is degrees either side of the required course that are relevant. To give an indication of the importance of this type of error it is only necessary to look at some very simple facts. Over 60 miles 1° of error in course steered will give approximately 1 mile of error at the end, and this could mean anything from 5 minutes to half an hour of wasted time. Thus it is obviously essential that these errors are minimimal, and where they cannot be made insignificant they must at least be allowed for.

The steering compasses are the most obvious source of possible error to the course steered and for your peace of mind as navigator they must be properly swung and adjusted with any remaining error noted down in an easily used format. What tends to happen on yachts with more than one compass is that the main, central compass is adjusted accurately while the wing compasses are ignored as being of only tactical importance. This has obvious disadvantages and should be avoided whenever possible. The other compass that is often installed as an afterthought is the navigator's telltale compass down below at the chart table. This is frequently sited next to instruments or wiring, over the engine and so on, in such a way as to be virtually uncorrectable. One excellent solution to this problem is to have the telltale compass as a repeater off the main compass. Assuming then that the compasses have all been adjusted as well as possible and are checked against transits, etc whenever convenient, there should be virtually zero error from them unless the sea is very rough when their damping may not be sufficient. Beware of beer cans, transistor radios, pairs of pliers and suchlike as these can have disastrous effects.

Helmsman error is undoubtedly the biggest single source of error in all your navigation problems and calculations, but this too can be largely allowed for with a bit of effort. The first thing to realize is that it doesn't really matter if the helmsman is steering a few degrees off course if this is making the boat go fast, so long as you know the actual course steered. To persuade the people who helm your boat to be honest is largely a matter of education: if you get annoyed every time you are told of a deviation from the required course then very soon you will get a situation where everybody says that they have been steering the right course even if this is not true. Right at the start of this book one aspect of this education process was looked at, the logbook data. Separate columns for the course given and the course actually steered indicate to the crew that you really do want them to be honest. Apart from this it is largely a matter of getting to know how all the helmsmen on your boat react in different conditions by watching them steer at the same time as keeping an eye on the course averaged. You can then compare their estimate of course steered with your own estimate.

Some fairly general guidelines can be also laid down. First, most compasses can only be read to within plus or minus 2° unless the course required is, by chance, one of the markings on the compass. So wherever possible give a sensible course to steer such as 290° rather than the ideal course of say 291°. Giving courses in this way enables the navigator to make the necessary allowances for the course being one degree wrong, rather than the helmsman having to try to make the same allowances.

The point of sailing also makes quite a difference to the actual course steered. Going upwind, a good helmsman will keep on trying to get the boat pointing just a bit higher all the time and this means that he is likely to notice his compass heading at the most advantageous time on each wind shift: thus his estimate of average course may well be 2°–3° higher than that sailed. Downwind, there are two very different situations. Square running, most helmsmen will shy away from running by the lee, so it is important not to give a course to steer that is too square (it's nearly always slow anyway). On a tight reach, the tendency will be to bear away in the gusts to stop broaching so the mean course will be to leeward of that required. Waves will also obviously make a big difference to the course, particularly a quartering sea. In really big waves the course alterations needed to get the most out of a boat could easily be around 20° to 30°.

To recap on helmsman errors, in light to moderate conditions an accuracy within 2°–3° of the required course should be possible with the helmsman being able to estimate his average course even more accurately than this, but as the conditions deteriorate the errors in course steered will increase up to plus or minus 20° or so at any given moment, and with a good helmsman this will probably average out to about 5° either side of course. An honest man would be unlikely to be able to estimate his course steered to better than about plus or minus 3° accuracy in this situation and an inexperienced helmsman might be farther out than this.

Tidal Streams

Various hydrographic authorities have spent considerable time and effort establishing the direction and rate of the tidal streams. The use of this information has already been looked at in Chapter 3 but it is important to reaffirm the sources of error in this data. In most areas detailed tidal stream (current) data is only available for specific waters where that information is needed by ships, for example in approach channels, around headlands etc. This means of course that close inshore and in bays the information available for smaller craft or yachtsmen to use is far more scanty, and less likely to be revised. Luckily, these areas tend to have weaker tides anyway. So 'local knowledge' and/or intelligent guesswork is required in order to be able to estimate the streams in such places. This could easily introduce a half knot error into your calculations.

The other major built-in source of potential errors in tidal stream predictions is that in most cases the streams are measured and predicted fairly accurately for *average* spring tides. The interpolation for the range of the tide for the day in question is, of necessity, based on a linear graph of the proportions between neaps and springs. Although this is the best interpolation that can be done, it is not always one hundred per cent correct and in my experience this factor alone can sometimes introduce an error on the order of 5 per cent or exceptionally up to 10 per cent into a single tidal stream calculation.

Finally, the meteorological conditions can have a profound effect on the tidal streams. The most common weather effect is a different time from that predicted for the change of tide. I have known this difference to be as much as three-quarters of an hour when there has been a strong wind blowing for several days. However, if the time of high water has been altered by say 30 minutes, the time of low water will not necessarily be changed by the same amount. This gives rise to a change in the duration of the tide which means that the same quantity of water is moving the same distance but in a different time, obviously altering the rate of the tidal stream accordingly. Assuming that the time differences we are talking about are in the order of 30 minutes, and the average duration of the tide is 6 hours, then the error in the rate of the tidal stream will most probably be about one-twelfth of the total, that is up to 8 per cent error.

To summarize tidal stream errors, in normal weather conditions and at spring tides the predictions are likely to be more or less accurate. In the same conditions at neaps, the predictions are quite likely to be 5 per cent out. In unusual weather the error could be up to 10 per cent in total but with intelligence one can to some extent predict the effects of the prevailing conditions and thus keep the error down. In areas with insufficient data the error will depend on one's experience in similar situations but could be up to half a knot.

Tidal Heights

It must also be remembered that tidal heights can be altered in similar ways to tidal streams. A high barometer, a long period of drought, or a stretch of freezing weather over the nearby hills can depress the level of water in an estuary by as much as a metre or more, especially if, as can easily happen, all phenomena occur simultaneously. In the other direction, a low glass and a southwesterly gale will raise the water level in areas such as the Clyde or the South Coast of England, as water is funnelled between the land masses.

The errors in tidal heights can be anticipated and determined to a large extent and therefore allowed for in your calculations. It is often worth comparing the actual depths found by echo-sounder with the predicted depths obtained from a combination of the chart and tide tables. The only real difficulty is likely to occur when a coast is being approached from the open sea, when initially at least there will be no hard evidence to work from to determine the tidal height. In this situation it is probably sensible to allow a little margin for safety.

Other Sources of Error

Mis-identification of fixing objects The navigational practices that one uses should be such that it is almost impossible to put a fix on the chart that is wrong due to the mis-identification of the objects used for that fix. At night always use a stopwatch to time lights, and check carefully that there is only one light with that characteristic. Never use a headland unless you are sure it is the right one. It is all too easy to misjudge how far you can see and thus be looking at a headland closer than the one wanted. Use all your available information even if it is merely to check an item of data, and finally, take three-point fixes if at all possible as you then have a check built in to the fix.

Changing charts One of the easiest ways to introduce gross error into your navigation. If the new chart that you are transferring to has the same scale as the old one then there is not much problem, but if it is a different scale there is scope for lots of mistakes! On one occasion during a simple 80 mile passage, I transferred my estimated position from one chart to the next, misread the scale and was 10 miles out because of it. I then made the situation even worse by rubbing out all the lines on the old chart before putting it away thus making it very difficult to check back at a later stage. Since then I have taken to double-checking a transfer of that sort by using two different methods to transfer the position. For example using lat. and long. for the transfer and checking it with a bearing and distance from a common point. There are obviously many ways of checking like this and for the extra time that it takes you it must be worthwhile.

RDF Position lines obtained from good radio direction finding sets are not necessarily much less accurate than other position lines; typically they may be accurate to $3°–5°$. However, the distances involved between yacht and radio station are normally far greater than with other methods of fixing, so the actual errors likely when using RDF can easily be very large, with cocked hats several miles long being realistic. As long as you always think of fixes as areas of probability this doesn't matter, but if you put an RDF fix on the chart as an exact position then you are looking for trouble.

Tiredness Although this is not in itself an error, a mention of tiredness is relevant in this chapter as fatigue is a major source of errors. When you are really tired every calculation takes more effort and every decision is more suspect. The message here is, on a long race be prepared beforehand with adequate rest and do not sit aimlessly at the chart table when you could be getting some sleep. In my experience there are quite enough times during a race when it is essential for the navigator to be awake without unnecessarily adding to these times.

Seasickness Most people find that it is almost impossible to spend long enough below to navigate accurately enough for racing once they start feeling seasick. Although it is quite easy to force yourself below to do an obviously essential job, it is far more difficult to make yourself go below to think about a decision or fact that might not be needed for some time or that might not be required at all. As a sometime sufferer from seasickness, my advice to would-be racing navigators is, don't be afraid to take a pill if this will stop the malady! If they don't work (and there are lots of different ones to try), how about being a foredeck hand instead of a navigator?

Areas of Probability

Apart from taking a mental note of all the errors that are possible or likely, as navigator, it is vital that we can allow for errors in as quantitative a way as possible. One way to do this is not to navigate with an estimated position on the chart but rather to navigate an area of probability around the chart. In order to look at the practicalities of this, let's take a hypothetical example of a 60 mile leg of a race.

Assuming it to be a cross-tide situation, the errors in distance run should only be the log, say 2–3 per cent or $1\frac{1}{2}$ miles. Course steered is unlikely to be more accurate than $\pm 2°$ which on this distance means ± 2 miles. If the total predicted tidal set for the leg is 20 miles and the predictions are accurate to ± 5 per cent this gives an error of 1 mile either side of the predicted position. Adding up all these errors, an area of probability 6 miles across and $1\frac{1}{2}$ miles long can be drawn as a sort of sausage and after this 60 mile leg this is as accurate as one could reasonably expect to be.

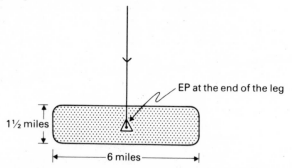

12.1 Area of probable position at the end of a hypothetical 60 miles

However, this is taking the worst case as it is quite likely that during a 60 mile leg at least one position fix will be possible, thus reducing the size of this sausage shape. Regardless of this likelihood, though, the percentage errors will still be the same so in the example quoted you would need to ensure that you were 3 miles to the correct side of the next turning mark in order not to risk being down-tide, square running to the mark, or whatever. In practice you need to have the area of probability since the last fix in mind and work within the limits that this ordains.

Appendices

APPENDIX 1

Morgan Cup Race – Tidal Heights

PORTSMOUTH (4.1 m, 2.0 m)

FRI	1653	1.1
	2353	4.5
SAT	0513	0.9
	1221	4.5
	1732	1.0
SUN	0031	4.5
	0552	0.8
	1300	4.5
	1813	0.9

DOVER (5.9 m, 3.3 m)

FRI	1121	5.0
	2333	5.2
SAT	1158	5.3
SUN	0011	5.4
	1236	5.5

PORTLAND (1.9 m, 0.7 m)

FRI	1931	1.9
SAT	0003	0.3
	0738	1.8
	1217	0.2
	2018	2.0
SUN	0043	0.3
	0826	1.9
	1256	0.2
	2059	2.1

ST HELIER (9.8 m, 4.0 m)

FRI	1851	8.0
SAT	0712	8.0
	1934	8.5
SUN	0753	8.6
	1437	8.6

DEVONPORT (4.7 m, 2.2 m)

FRI	1812	5.1
SAT	0024	1.1
	0633	5.1
	1243	1.0
	1856	5.2
SUN	0107	0.9
	0719	5.1
	1326	0.9
	1940	5.3

CHERBOURG (Heights)

FRI	2026	5.9
SAT	0846	5.9
	2106	6.1
SUN	0926	6.0
	2147	6.2

Place	2030	2130	2230	2330	0030	0130	0230	0330	0430	(Friday Night and Saturday Morning)
PORTSMOUTH	2.3	2.9	3.7	4.3	4.4					
RYDE	2.4	3.1	3.9	4.2	4.2					
BRADING	1.4	1.8	2.3	2.8	2.8					
SANDOWN	2.3	2.9	3.4	3.7	3.6	3.3	2.6			
VENTNOR		2.9	3.3	3.6	3.5	3.1	2.4			
FRESHWATER			2.3	2.2	2.2	2.0	1.5			
CHRISTCHURCH					1.5	1.3	0.9	0.6	0.4	
POOLE					1.5	1.5	1.2	0.8	0.8	
SWANAGE					1.3	1.3	1.1	0.7	0.8	
LULWORTH					0.6	0.7	0.6	0.6	1.0	
PORTLAND					0.4	0.6	0.5	0.5	0.8	

Place	1100	1200	1300	1400	1500	1600	1700	1800	1900	2000	2100	2200	2300	0000
OMMONVILLE	4.5	3.6	2.7	2.0	1.5	1.6	2.3	3.7	4.9	5.7	6.0	6.3	5.9	5.0
CHERBOURG	4.5	3.6	2.7	1.9	1.5	1.5	2.2	3.6	5.0	5.8	5.9	5.8	5.0	4.0
BARFLEUR	5.5	4.7	3.7	2.8	2.0	1.6	1.6	2.4	3.8	5.1	6.0	6.3	5.9	5.0

Interpolation Table for Tidal Stream Rates – Portsmouth

Mean rate of stream (knots)		Range of the tide at Portsmouth (metres)																	
Np	Sp	1.6	1.8	2.0	2.2	2.4	2.6	2.8	3.0	3.2	3.4	3.6	3.8	4.0	4.2	4.4	4.6	4.8	5.0
0.1	0.2	01	01	01	01	01	01	01	02	02	02	02	02	02	02	02	02	02	02
0.2	0.4	02	02	02	02	02	03	03	03	03	03	04	04	04	04	04	04	05	05
0.3	0.6	02	03	03	03	03	04	04	04	05	05	05	06	06	06	06	07	07	07
0.4	0.8	03	04	04	04	05	05	06	06	06	07	07	07	08	08	09	09	09	10
0.5	1.0	04	05	05	05	06	06	07	07	08	08	09	09	10	10	11	11	12	12
0.6	1.2	05	05	06	07	07	08	08	09	09	10	10	11	12	12	13	14	14	15
0.7	1.4	06	06	07	08	08	09	10	10	11	12	12	13	14	14	15	16	16	17
0.8	1.6	06	07	08	09	10	10	11	12	13	13	14	15	16	16	17	18	19	19
0.9	1.8	07	08	09	10	11	12	12	13	14	15	16	17	18	18	19	20	21	22
1.0	2.0	08	09	10	11	12	13	14	15	16	17	18	19	20	20	21	22	23	24
1.1	2.2	09	10	11	12	13	14	15	16	17	18	19	20	22	22	24	25	26	27
1.2	2.4	10	11	12	13	14	15	17	18	19	20	21	22	23	25	26	27	28	29
1.3	2.6	11	12	13	14	15	17	18	19	20	22	23	24	25	27	28	29	30	32
1.4	2.8	11	13	14	15	17	18	19	21	22	23	25	26	27	29	30	31	33	34
1.5	3.0	12	14	15	16	18	19	21	22	24	25	26	28	29	31	32	34	35	36
1.6	3.2	13	14	16	18	19	21	22	24	25	27	28	30	31	33	34	36	37	39
1.7	3.4	14	15	17	19	20	22	23	25	27	28	30	32	33	35	36	38	40	41
1.8	3.6	15	16	18	20	21	23	25	27	28	30	32	33	35	37	39	40	42	44
1.9	3.8	16	17	19	21	23	24	26	28	30	32	33	35	37	39	41	43	44	46
2.0	4.0	16	18	20	22	24	26	28	30	32	33	36	37	39	41	43	44	47	48

Interpolation Table for Tidal Stream Rates – Devonport

Mean rate of stream (knots)		Range of tide at Devonport (metres)																				
Np	Sp	1.6	1.8	2.0	2.2	2.4	2.6	2.8	3.0	3.2	3.4	3.6	3.8	4.0	4.2	4.4	4.6	4.7	4.8	5.0	5.2	5.4
0.1	0.2	01	01	01	01	01	01	01	01	01	01	02	02	02	02	02	02	02	02	02	02	02
0.2	0.4	02	02	02	02	02	02	02	03	03	03	03	03	03	04	04	04	04	04	04	04	05
0.3	0.6	02	03	03	03	03	03	04	04	04	04	05	05	05	05	06	06	06	06	06	07	07
0.4	0.8	03	03	04	04	04	05	05	05	06	06	06	07	07	07	08	08	08	08	08	09	09
0.5	1.0	04	04	05	05	05	06	06	07	07	07	08	08	09	09	09	10	10	10	11	11	11
0.6	1.2	05	05	06	06	06	07	07	08	08	09	09	10	10	11	11	12	12	12	13	13	14
0.7	1.4	05	06	06	07	08	08	09	09	10	10	11	11	12	13	13	14	14	14	15	15	16
0.8	1.6	06	07	07	08	09	09	10	11	11	12	12	13	14	14	15	16	16	16	17	18	18
0.9	1.8	07	08	08	09	10	10	11	12	13	13	14	15	15	16	17	18	18	18	19	20	21
1.0	2.0	08	08	09	10	11	12	12	13	14	15	16	16	17	18	19	20	20	20	21	22	23
1.1	2.2	08	09	10	11	12	13	14	15	15	16	17	18	19	20	21	22	22	22	23	24	25
1.2	2.4	09	10	11	12	13	14	15	16	17	18	19	20	21	22	23	24	24	24	25	26	27
1.3	2.6	10	11	12	13	14	15	16	17	18	19	20	21	22	23	24	25	26	27	28	29	30
1.4	2.8	11	12	13	14	15	16	17	18	20	21	22	23	24	25	26	27	28	29	30	31	32
1.5	3.0	11	13	14	15	16	17	19	20	21	22	23	25	26	27	28	29	30	31	32	33	34
1.6	3.2	12	13	15	16	17	19	20	21	22	24	25	26	28	29	30	31	32	33	34	35	36
1.7	3.4	13	14	16	17	18	20	21	22	24	25	27	28	29	31	32	33	34	35	36	37	39
1.8	3.6	14	15	17	18	19	21	22	24	25	27	28	30	31	32	34	35	36	37	38	40	41
1.9	3.8.	14	16	17	19	21	22	24	25	27	28	30	31	33	34	36	37	38	39	40	42	43
2.0	4.0	15	17	18	20	22	23	25	26	28	30	31	33	34	36	38	39	40	41	42	44	46
2.1	4.2	16	18	19	21	23	24	26	28	29	31	33	34	36	38	39	41	42	43	45	46	48
2.2	4.4	17	18	20	22	24	26	27	29	31	33	34	36	38	40	41	43	44	45	47	48	50

Downwind Tacking Angles

Angle	Alion % Distance Increase	Alion Speed Increase required to make good extra distance									
		2 kt	2.5 kt	3 kt	4 kt	5 kt	6 kt	7 kt	8 kt	9 kt	10 kt
5°	0.3%	0.01	0.01	0.01	0.01	0.02	0.02	0.02	0.02	0.03	0.03
10°	1.4%	0.03	0.03	0.04	0.06	0.07	0.08	0.1	0.11	0.13	0.14
15°	3%	0.06	0.07	0.09	0.12	0.15	0.18	0.21	0.24	0.27	0.3
20°	6%	0.12	0.15	0.18	0.24	0.3	0.36	0.42	0.48	0.54	0.6
25°	10%	0.2	0.25	0.3	0.4	0.5	0.6	0.7	0.8	0.9	1.0
30°	15%	0.3	0.37	0.45	0.6	0.75	0.9	1.1	1.2	1.4	1.5
35°	22%	0.4	0.6	0.7	0.9	1.1	1.3	1.5	1.8	2.0	2.2
37.5°	25%	0.5	0.6	0.75	1.0	1.25	1.5	1.75	2.0	2.25	2.5
40°	30%	0.6	0.75	0.9	1.2	1.5	1.8	2.1	2.4	2.7	3.0
42.5°	34%	0.7	0.9	1.0	1.4	1.7	2.0	2.4	2.7	3.0	3.4
45°	40%	0.8	1.0	1.2	1.6	2.0	2.4	2.8	3.2	3.6	4.0